PHYSIOLOGICAL
AND BEHAVIORAL ASPECTS
OF TASTE

CONTRIBUTORS

ROBERT B. MacLEOD

MORLEY R. KARE

HARRY L. JACOBS

RALPH L. KITCHELL

GABRIEL P. FROMMER

FRANCIS J. PILGRIM

KENT R. CHRISTENSEN

JAY TEPPERMAN

FRANKLIN W. HEGGENESS

HERBERT L. PICK, JR.

CARL PFAFFMANN

PHYSIOLOGICAL
AND
BEHAVIORAL ASPECTS
OF TASTE

Edited by
MORLEY R. KARE
and
BRUCE P. HALPERN

THE UNIVERSITY OF CHICAGO PRESS

Library of Congress Catalog Card Number 61-15937

THE UNIVERSITY OF CHICAGO PRESS, CHICAGO & LONDON

The University of Toronto Press, Toronto 5, Canada

PARTICIPANTS

L. M. BARTLETT
Department of Zoology, University of Massachusetts, Amherst, Mass.

ROBERT M. BENJAMIN
Department of Physiology, Service Memorial Institutes, University of Wisconsin, Madison, Wis.

RUDY A. BERNARD
Department of Physiology, New York State Veterinary College, Cornell University, Ithaca, N.Y.

JOHN A. CARPENTER
Laboratory of Applied Biodynamics, Yale University, New Haven, Conn.

KENT R. CHRISTENSEN
Department of Psychology, University of Illinois, Urbana, Ill.

WILLIAM C. DILGER
Laboratory of Ornithology, Cornell University, Ithaca, N.Y.

TRYGG ENGEN
Department of Psychology, Brown University, Providence, R.I.

IRVING Y. FISHMAN
Department of Biology, Division of Natural Sciences, Grinnell College, Grinnell, Iowa

GABRIEL P. FROMMER
Department of Psychology, Brown University, Providence, R.I.

ALLAN C. GOLDSTEIN
Department of Psychology, Cornell University, Ithaca, N.Y.

EDGAR B. HALE
Departments of Poultry Husbandry and Psychology, Pennsylvania State University, State College, Pa.

BRUCE P. HALPERN
Departments of Psychology and Veterinary Physiology, Cornell University, Ithaca, N.Y.

ARTHUR E. HARRIMAN
Department of Psychology, Franklin and Marshall College, Lancaster, Pa.

FRANKLIN W. HEGGENESS
Department of Physiology, University of Rochester School of Medicine, Rochester, N.Y.

HARRY L. JACOBS
Department of Physiology, University of Rochester School of Medicine, Rochester, N.Y.

MORLEY R. KARE
Department of Physiology, New York State Veterinary College, Cornell University, Ithaca, N.Y.

RALPH L. KITCHELL
Division of Anatomy, College of Veterinary Medicine, University of Minnesota, St. Paul, Minn.

ROBERT B. MACLEOD
Department of Psychology, Cornell University, Ithaca, N.Y.

G. ROLFE MORRISON
Department of Psychology, McMaster University, Hamilton, Ont.

ROSE MARIE PANGBORN
Department of Food Science and Technology, University of California, Davis, Calif.

HERBERT L. PICK, JR.*
Department of Psychology, Cornell University, Ithaca, N.Y.

FRANCIS J. PILGRIM
Quartermaster Food and Container Institute, Chicago, Ill.

MARTIN W. SCHEIN
Department of Poultry Husbandry, Pennsylvania State University, State College, Pa.

JAY TEPPERMAN
Department of Pharmacology, State University of New York Upstate Medical Center, Syracuse, N.Y.

L. F. TITLEBAUM
Department of Nutrition, Harvard University School of Public Health, Boston, Mass.

* Paper submitted subsequent to conference.

Preface

Carl Pfaffmann

P HYSIOLOGICAL PSYCHOLOGISTS pose for themselves the task of attempting to understand behavior in terms of its underlying physiology. In a sense their work derives from two heritages: the one, a molar, purely behavioral or psychological; the second, a more mechanism-oriented physiological tradition. Often scholars in other disciplines have difficulty deciding what distinguishes a psychologist from his physiologist colleague who may be working upon the same or similar problems in the next laboratory. One common distinction is that the psychologist's major concern is with behavior, the end result of the $S-R$ chain of events initiated by the stimulus. In recent years there has been a growing interest in the study of behavior on the part of many biological workers, and arbitrary distinctions and dividing lines between disciplines are becoming increasingly difficult to draw and to maintain. Another consequence of this trend is the occurrence on the scientific calendar of many interdisciplinary symposia such as the present one.

Early physiological psychology was often naïve in its attempt to find a direct physiological counterpart for some psychological process or event. Thus it was hoped that measurement of inspiration/expiration ratio of breathing, or the psychogalvanic response, for example, might be a good index of "emotion," such physiological measures usually being treated as isomorphic with the psychological process. Today we recognize that many psychological terms represent more properly hypothetical constructs, not substantive entities. It is unlikely that any *one* physiological measure is isomorphic with any *one* psychological process. In short, early physiological psychologists seemed to be searching for physiological unities directly paralleling the psychic ones. This strategy often failed, for, as Skinner (1953) and others have pointed out, much early physiological psychology often only gave physiological names to relations derived from purely behavioral observation. The "neural trace" of the conditioned response, for example, is still largely a statement of faith that there must be a neural change basic to learning. What or where such a "trace" might be is still largely an unanswered problem.

The danger of pseudo-physiologizing about psychology is ever present. Even now the search goes on to find a magic molecule, be it serotonin or a hunger hormone, which might prove to be the single or essential determinant of some highly complex behavior or behavioral deviation. But, increasingly, the evidence suggests that several different *physiological mechanisms* may be involved in any one psychological process. I doubt that there will be a simple isomorphism between physiology and psychology. The connection between the two domains might better be characterized as a functional relationship which often is complicated and obscured by the fact that, in mathematical terms, the function may be non-linear or even non-monotonic.

A somewhat classical example of the problem of relating physiology to psychology, but one relevant to this symposium, may be found in the question of the basic qualities of taste. Phenomenology or direct experience reveals the existence of a number of different taste dimensions of which *salty, sour, bitter,* and *sweet* were said to be basic or primary. If one traces the history of the classification of taste sensation, we find that varying numbers and kinds of taste qualities had been proposed by different workers at one time or another. The problem is still with us, for even in this symposium the question has come up, although the point no longer leads to excesses of debate. Most people consider these terms as basic only in the sense that they are convenient and well-known labels for the more commonly perceived taste dimensions.

The concept of the basic or primary tastes derived largely from the elementaristic view of mental life promulgated by the introspective psychologists following the lead of the nineteenth-century sense physiologists. The phenomenon of color mixture in the visual modality showed, most strikingly, that complex visual experiences could be produced by a mixture of only three primary wave lengths. The theory of three basic color receptors followed quite naturally. This model coupled with the dominant doctrine of specific nerve energies was quickly applied to the other modalities. It was generally accepted that most sense organs were composed of only a few primary receptors and their associated nerve fibers, and thus that most taste experiences resulted from the combined stimulation of the basic taste receptors, complicated perhaps by additional components from the other modalities of the mouth. It is not my purpose to review the long history of this controversy, for others have done this in a more scholarly manner (Boring, 1942, 1950). It would appear that the *Zeitgeist* of the nineteenth century was responsible in large measure for the dogma of the four fundamental taste qualities.

Actually I too began my early electrophysiological studies (Pfaffmann, 1941) in search of the basic taste receptors. But it soon became apparent that the correspondence between the "basic four" and physiological types did not exist, at least in the animal preparation. I extended these investigations as did other workers (Cohen *et al.*, 1955; Fishman, 1957; Pfaffmann, 1955; and Zotterman, 1958), and it is now quite clear that in no organism so far investigated, including primates, are there primary taste receptor types—at least as I read the evidence. Furthermore, the important work of Kimura and Beidler (1956) showed that the multiple sensitivity of many individual afferent fibers from the tongue may also be found in the individual receptor cells of the taste bud. Thus one and the same chemoreceptor cell will be reactive to NaCl and sucrose or to NaCl and HCl, for example. Taste receptor cells are differentially sensitive to chemicals, but they are not rigidly specific. In this symposium, reference has also been made to the fact that a temporal patterning in the discharge often distinguishes the discharge to sucrose stimulus. Perhaps such temporal characteristics provide a basis for discrimination. In any case the weight of the evidence suggests that the afferent neural code depends upon the patterning of input.

Most recently, Beidler (1960, 1962) has shown that the taste cells themselves appear to have a relatively brief life and that they are in a continuous state of flux and change. Taste cells appear to be produced by mitotic division of epithelium at the edges of the bud. Then as they age they migrate toward the center of the taste bud and apparently disintegrate and disappear to be continually replaced by new cells. The individual taste cell appears to have a turnover rate of some six to eight days as observed by a labeling technique for cells treated with tritiated thymidine. While there is a continual turnover of cells in the normal life of the taste bud, the afferent nerve fibers themselves of course do not degenerate. They are relatively fixed, but presumably their fine unmyelinated endings make and break connections as taste cells come and go. It is not known whether the receptor-nerve contact during the life of the taste cell is permanent or also in a continual state of flux as cells move from periphery to center. This is an important point to settle.

We have recently studied a related phenomenon in the taste electrophysiological response of tongues irradiated with X-rays (Pfaffmann, C., F. G. Sherman, R. A. Ellis, and J. B. Powers, "The effect of X-ray irradiation upon taste sensitivity." In preparation). A single dose of 1,500 to 5,000 R does not grossly affect the response in the chorda tympani nerve as monitored by electrophysiological recording until after the sixth day post-irradiation when the response drops off rapidly. Within the six-day post-irradiation period however, there is a gradual quantitative drop in magnitude of the chorda tympani response to NaCl whereas the response to sucrose seems to remain constant or even increases somewhat. At the sixth to seventh day the response to sucrose and NaCl both drop off rapidly.

X-ray irradiation is known to stop mitotic cell division in epithelial tissue. It can be argued therefore that during the post-irradiation period the turnover process described by Beidler (1960, 1962) continues for taste cells already differentiated but that there is no replacement by mitosis. The population of taste cells therefore is gradually aging and declining in size. As cells grow older it seems that they change their relative responsivity to NaCl and to sucrose. Thus mixed population of new and old cells in the normal preparation may be more NaCl than sucrose sensitive, but the older cell population after radiation appears relatively more sensitive to sucrose, assuming that the changing electrophysiological picture reflects changes in sensitivity of taste cells and not specific radiation effects.

The afferent nerve fibers make physical synaptic-type contact with the taste cells. At the present time it is not clear how the changing anatomical relation between taste cell and afferent nerve ending influences the afferent code in any one fiber as the receptor cells go through the turn-over cycle. Chronic micro-electrode studies in the *CNS*, perhaps in the medulla or in the thalamus, might show whether the individual cells of the sensory relay retain a fixed pattern of sensitivity or whether they too show a "turnover of sensitivity." Whatever the outcome of future studies, it seems clear that the classical physiological isomorphy between receptor types and psychologically basic taste qualities is highly questionable. Just what the new conception will be remains for the future.

As I have indicated in another publication (Pfaffmann, 1959a), these considerations are not unique to taste alone. There is increasing evidence of patterning in the cutaneous system (Wall, 1960; Weddell, 1955). In audition the temporal pattern of the volley mechanism has long been recognized (Wever, 1949). That discrimination depends on differential receptor sensitivity is unequivocally clear, but we are still looking for a precise statement of the relationship between neural mechanisms and the psychophysical and phenomenal features of sensation.

In a more general way, the sense of taste has much to recommend it to the behavior scientist. The senses play many roles in the life of the organism. Traditionally they have been called the avenues to knowledge of the world; in more contemporary terms, "channels for sensory communication." Some sense organs seem to be especially noteworthy for the amount and variety of information which they can transmit. Vision and hearing lie at the top of the sensory hierarchy in richness of cognitive detail, variety of sensory experience, and significance for perception. On the other hand, the sense organs may subserve another behavioral function, that of mediating or providing motivational value. Here the lower senses, like taste, are particularly noteworthy. Gustatory stimuli can and do instigate strong acceptance or rejection responses. Certain solutions made up of taste stimuli are highly palatable and will be taken in preference to water or other solutions when a free choice is given. Furthermore, when these solutions are used as reinforcers in a learning situation, the acquisition of behavior is rapid and dramatic. An animal will learn a bar-pressing response for sucrose and even for non-nutritive "sweet" solutions. I refer here to primary reinforcing effects, for there is almost no limit to the secondary motivating properties which any stimulus may acquire as a result of learning. At the same time certain taste stimuli will elicit strong reactions of disgust in man or extreme pleasure. We speak of these as hedonic responses, the pleasures or displeasures of sensation presumably reflecting related processes which in the animal are basic to preference and aversion responses (Pfaffmann, 1960). The property of taste stimuli which instigates strong consummatory responses, elicits preference or avoidance behavior, provides reinforcement in learning situations, and elicits hedonic responses in man makes it of particular interest to the behavior scientist. The sense of taste is a specific sensory-neural system whose peripheral and central response mechanisms have been increasingly revealed by recent active experimentation, some of which is described in this symposium. Furthermore, an increasing behavior technology is making it possible to carry out an analysis of the gustatory control of behavior, both with regard to its cue value and motivational significance.

The fact that sensory stimuli have both cognitive and motivational functions is perhaps more obvious in the case of taste than for a number of other senses, particularly with regard to the positively rewarding or adient aspects of stimulation. Other senses have unlearned motivational consequences but these tend to be aversive. Bright light, for example, is a strong aversive stimulus, but dim light is only a relatively weak positive reinforcer (for example, Kish, 1955; Kling *et al.*, 1956; Marx *et al.*, 1955). Strong sounds are aversive, but attempts to show positively rewarding effects of weak auditory stimuli have not been successful (Barnes, G. W., and G. B. Kish, 1961, Reinforcing properties of the onset of auditory stimulation. Personal communication). The effect of sucrose solution as a positive reinforcer of bar-pressing or of quinine as an aversive stimulus is equally striking. Thus the sense of taste provides strong positive as well as negative reinforcement. Because of its specific sensory properties, we can regard the sense of taste as a model stimulus-response system for the purpose of making a physiological analysis. When the gustatory afferent input and its subsequent neural ramifications have been completely analyzed, we should have a clearer idea of the physiological processes basic to the process of reinforcement. Principles of importance not only for the understanding of sensory functions but for behavior theory in general should emerge.

It is because of these "two faces" to the sense of taste that this symposium includes studies devoted to methodology, purely sensory processes, central neural mechanisms, comparative studies of taste preferences together with the factors influencing them, and finally the relation between nutrition, metabolism, behavior, and taste. All are aspects of the central theme on the *gustatory control of behavior*.

Acknowledgments

THIS BOOK is based upon a transcript of a conference held at Cornell University in June, 1960. It is appropriate to recognize at this time the assistance and encouragement of Dr. H. H. Dukes in conducting these conferences.

The contribution of all the participants in both the symposium and the subsequent publication is acknowledged. We are grateful for the special co-operation in organizing the meeting and editing the transcript by Drs. R. B. MacLeod, M. W. Schein, and E. B. Hale. For help in so many ways we would also thank Dr. M. S. Ficken and Mrs. L. Larson.

This conference and the preparation of the manuscript for publication were financially supported by the National Science Foundation Grant No. G12866. Assistance was also received from the National Institutes of Health (National Institute of Neurological Diseases and Blindness Grant No. B2184).

Acknowledgements

Contents

1. WHAT IS A SENSE?   1
   Robert B. MacLeod

2. COMPARATIVE ASPECTS OF THE SENSE OF TASTE   6
   Morley R. Kare

   THE OSMOTIC POSTINGESTION FACTOR IN THE REGULATION
       OF GLUCOSE APPETITE   16
   Harry L. Jacobs

   DISCUSSION   27

3. NEURAL RESPONSE PATTERNS IN TASTE   39
   Ralph L. Kitchell

   DISCUSSION   48

   GUSTATORY AFFERENT RESPONSES IN THE THALAMUS   50
   Gabriel P. Frommer

   DISCUSSION   62

4. INTERACTIONS OF SUPRATHRESHOLD TASTE STIMULI   66
   Francis J. Pilgrim

   DISCUSSION   72

   METHODOLOGY IN PREFERENCE TESTING   79
   Kent R. Christensen

   DISCUSSION   86

5. METABOLIC AND TASTE INTERACTIONS   92
   Jay Tepperman

   DISCUSSION   98

   METABOLIC FACTORS IN FOOD INTAKE AND UTILIZATION IN
       WEANLING RATS   104
   Franklin W. Heggeness

   DISCUSSION   109

6. Research on Taste in the Soviet Union   117
     Herbert L. Pick, Jr.

7. Summaries by Discussants   127
     Martin W. Schein
     Irving Y. Fishman
     Trygg Engen
     Edgar B. Hale

Bibliography   135

Index   147

CHAPTER 1

What Is a Sense?

Robert B. MacLeod

THE PAPERS in this symposium are all concerned with certain aspects of the "sense of taste." In an interdisciplinary enterprise such as this, it is inevitable that representatives of the co-operating sciences will have different conceptions of what it is we are talking about and what it is we are looking for. Have we a common meaning for the expression "sense of taste"? Have we, in fact, a common meaning for the word "sense"? At the risk of adding to our confusion, I propose to take a quick glance back at the history of the concept and to examine a few of its changing definitions. What will emerge, I fear, will be nothing more than a slight reformulation of the problem; but this is sometimes one of the ways in which science progresses.

The problem of the senses goes back to the earliest records of philosophic speculation. The early Greeks distinguished between appearance and reality, between the senses and the intellect. The senses were notoriously fallible. Only reason could probe through the veil of sensation and arrive at truth. Aristotle was by no means the first to give us a classification of the senses, but, since his five-fold system is what has come down to us through history, we might as well accept it as a provisional starting point. For Aristotle the senses were structures unique to animals and men. Plants could grow and reproduce but could not have sensation. Animals could sense their environments and move in response to sensations, but they could not think. Only man possessed the ability to integrate the data of sense and interpret rationally what he perceived. For Aristotle the senses were thus gateways, channels through which information from the outside world is transmitted to the perceiving organism. Aristotle recognized five senses—vision, hearing, smell, taste, and touch. A sixth, or common, sense permitted the integration of the data of these into unified percepts.

The five-fold classification would seem obvious. We have eyes for seeing, ears for hearing, noses for smelling, tongues for tasting, and skins for feeling. Such was the prestige of Aristotle that for more than two thousand years his five-fold classification remained essentially un-challenged. Even today we find people talking romantically of the five senses and occasionally speculating as to whether there may be a sixth sense, presumably extrasensory perception.

During modern times scientific interest in the senses begins with the philosophies of the late seventeenth and early eighteenth centuries. By the end of the eighteenth century, the new revolution in the physical sciences, and to a lesser extent in the biological sciences, had taken a firm grip on the imagination of the Western world. In 1687 Sir Isaac Newton published his *Principia*. In 1690 John Locke published his *Essay concerning the Human Understanding*. The relation between the two is not accidental. Newton's great synthesis presented us with a pic-ture of the material world composed of minute particles existing in ab-solute space and absolute time, propelled by force into motion or change of motion. All physical processes could theoretically be reduced to these simple terms. It is a tribute to Newton's greatness that, in spite of the twentieth-century revolution in physical theory, the mechanics and the optics of Newton are still sufficient for the analysis of a wide array of physical problems. The challenge to John Locke was to find a place in the Newtonian universe for a perceiving mind, and this is what he un-dertook to do in his *Essay*.

It is customary to disparage Locke's distinction between the primary and secondary qualities of sense, but in his day this was a reasonable distinction. The primary qualities were, literally, the properties of the physical world that Newton was talking about; namely, extension, dura-tion, mass, motion, and the like. The senses for Locke were still gate-ways through which correct information about the outside world could be received. It was clear to Locke, however, that perception contains much more than the primary qualities. There are also the reds and the blues, the sweets and the sours; in fact, all the qualities that seem to be uniquely related to the specific senses. These, Locke argued, must be contributed by the perceiving organism, and these he called the second-ary qualities of sense. We all recognize now that this distinction be-tween what comes in from without and what is supplied by the perceiv-ing organism is illicit, and the philosopher Berkeley had no difficulty in demolishing Locke's argument. What is important, however, is that Locke pointed in a very concrete way to the fact that the senses are not merely gateways but also shapers of our sensory experience. By the end of the eighteenth century, the sciences of anatomy and physiology were prepared for a direct study of the actual machinery whereby sensations of different sorts are aroused.

The story of the nineteenth century is an exciting one. The physicists were busy analyzing the physical processes, particularly in light and sound, which could constitute adequate stimuli for sensory reactions.

Anatomists and physiologists quickly gave up the traditional notion that there is a single sense of sight, a single sense of sound, etc. Buoyed up by the faith that for every qualitatively discriminable kind of sensation there must be a correspondingly differentiated sense receptor, they proceeded avidly to search for receptor mechanisms. The unity of the eye as a sense organ rapidly broke down as the conviction grew that there must be separate receptors, special mechanisms, for black and white, for red, blue, and green, and possibly even for yellow. The same thing was happening in audition, and in due course there was a search for receptor mechanisms in the tongue corresponding to sweet, sour, bitter, and salty. The story about smell and the cutaneous sensations is a different one, and more of that later.

At any rate, Aristotle's five senses were quickly multiplied many times over. Paralleling, and even more exciting than the quest for sense organs, were the studies of what happens after a sense receptor has been aroused. The story begins with the distinction, known as the Bell-Magendie Law, between the differing functions of afferent and efferent fibers. This was sufficient to inspire Johannes Müller to formulate the law of specific energies of nerves, a principle which was later to be elaborated to its limit by Helmholtz. Stated very crudely, the law asserts that the primary differentiation between one sensation and another is not to be found in the physical stimulus itself, nor is it to be found in the receptor process as such.

The real differentiation takes place in the central portions of the brain, where the nerve fibers terminate. When we perceive a color, said Müller, we perceive, not a property of the physical world, not a process in our receptors, but rather a condition of our central nerve endings. If we follow the Müller-Helmholtz logic to its limit, the problem of sensation becomes finally a central problem for the neurophysiologist. Regardless of peripheral processes of stimulation and reception, the real mystery of sensation lies in the brain, and presumably, in the cerebral cortex. If Müller's faith is justified, someday we shall be able to play by direct stimulation on the cortex and produce with complete confidence in our control all the sensory qualities which have been traditionally assigned to the sense organs. How closely have we approached this goal? I think you will agree that, in spite of the exciting, even glamorous, studies of cortical localization of function, we have still a long way to go. Through direct electrical stimulation of the cortex, we can now produce flashes of color, tones, noises, and even certain fairly predictable pressures and pains. We still have not the slightest idea, however, what in the cortex differentiates a red from a blue or a sweet from a sour. We believe that there must be appropriate processes there, but we have not yet found them.

I have been talking so far about philosophy, physics, anatomy, neurology, and physiology. All have been involved in the study of the senses. This is a truly interdisciplinary field. I hazard the guess that ten years hence the bulk of our discussion will be centered about biochemistry and biophysics; and, who knows, we may even be bringing in geology and astronomy. Where does psychology fit in? As a psychologist, I have naturally reserved this as my crowning point. Psychology deals with experience and behavior. On the human level we have the evidence of directly reportable experience. When we study animals, we may only deduce from their behavior what they presumably experience. Some psychologists—the behaviorists—insist that we should limit our study of man to the data obtainable from our non-linguistic cousins, the chimpanzees, the monkeys, the rats, and the chickens. It is not impossible to translate sensations and perceptions into discrimination responses. I have no real objection to this, except that it is very cumbersome. I have great respect for the chickens and the monkeys, but I think that we humans have a distinct advantage in that we can report our experience in a somewhat more discriminating language. I am all in favor of learning what we can from the animals, but I insist that we humans are still asking the questions. Until the animals conquer the world, human psychology will take precedence over animal psychology.

Let us return to the original question—what is a sense? A merely physical definition is obviously inadequate. Can we define it anatomically or physiologically? I do not think we can. We are still struggling to find sense receptors in the eye and the ear which are responsive to the variables in the physical world. We still do not know physically, physiologically, or anatomically what differentiates red from blue. So, we finally come back to psychology, and this is where smell and touch are so interesting. We can dissect out a multitude of so-called smell receptors in the nasal epithelium, and we can track down a multitude of olfactory fibers. We can excise a whole flock of possible subcutaneous receptors, Meissner corpuscles, Krause's end bulbs, free nerve endings, etc., but we still do not know what they do. We can spot the regions in the cortex which seem to be connected with some of our most distinctive sensations, but we still do not know what is going on.

The final point I should like to make—and this is possibly in defense of psychology—is that it is direct human experience which tells us what we should look for. We are looking for smell qualities, taste qualities, warm and cold and pressure and pain receptors. We would not know what to look for if we had not experienced the sensations first. What is a sense? I suggest that we give up the concept. There is no such thing as a sense. We have dimensions and qualities of sensation, and these can be measured. We have limitless forms of organization of the phenomenal world, only a few of which we can deal with scientifically. Someday we shall be able to translate into simple quantitative language the relation between the world about us and the world we experience.

If I may be permitted to end on a sort of moral note, may I suggest that we stop talking about taste and smell, vision and hearing as sensory systems, that we look first at the dimensions of human sensory experience and then try to identify their neurological, their physiological, their anatomical, and their physical correlates.

CHAPTER 2

Comparative Aspects of the Sense of Taste

Morley R. Kare

A CHARACTERISTIC of living matter is its sensitivity to the chemistry of its environment. The undifferentiated response of the amoeba to an acid stimulus is an example of primitive chemical reception which might appropriately be described as irritability. Some refinements of chemo-receptor apparatus are evident in animals with little trace of a central nervous system. Parker (1922) describes the departure from primitive irritability as the separation of the chemical and tactile senses. He cites the example of the sea anemone which responds at a different location to the application of meat juice than it does to a tactile stimulus.

Specialization and localization of the receptors seem to have occurred during evolution. The common chemical sense, differentiated from taste by the absence of specialized end-organs, generally has a higher thresh-old for various chemicals. Further, it is characterized by sensitive areas diffusely distributed over the body. The other extreme is illustrated in the higher animals where taste end-organs are sensitive to extreme dilution, are largely limited to the oral cavity, and exhibit greater specificity for chemical structure.

The intermediate situation occurring in fish was recently reviewed by Hasler (1957). Here the taste organs are distributed over the outer surfaces of the body. The report of Breder and Rasquin (1943) is of special evolutionary interest. They described the increased number of taste buds on the blind, cave-dwelling characin as compared to closely related, normal-eyed river fish. The amphibians exhibit a more ad-vanced condition than fish. They have a moist skin which responds to some chemicals but, unlike fish, their taste buds are limited to the oral cavity.

The localization of buds in the mouth and pharynx is common to the "air inhabiting" vertebrates. Histologically, these structures are essen-tially similar in all the animals we work with (rats, dogs, pigs, calves, and chickens). This observation is made, not to minimize the differences, but rather to emphasize the common general pattern.

The presence of taste buds and the ability to discriminate between chemical solutions certainly are not evidence that an animal shares man's taste sensations. Without committing man to a category of sensory decadence, one must recognize that a given animal whose nervous development is substantially less than that in man can exceed him in a particular sensory capacity. In any event, it is obvious that we cannot consider the lower animal as living in a replica of man's sensory world. My presentations will support the contention that the taste world of various animals is truly different from our own.

Laboratory and domestic animals have been bred for many generations without selection for the ability to taste. Since many such animals have no choice in diet, taste acuity would be of no survival value. However, this procedure of selection may have favored animals whose sensory endowments would be insufficient to permit them to survive under conditions other than that of the laboratory or farm.

The maintenance of adequate nutrition is a function commonly assigned to taste. Excluding a situation where starvation is a factor, wild animals do not commonly suffer from self-imposed malnutrition. It seems reasonable to attribute this selection of a nutritionally adequate diet to taste and the other senses. The taste aspects of this hypothesis were tested with domestic fowl in our laboratory; the results were contradictory. While there was some evidence of inherent wisdom in correcting a nutritional deficiency in a two-choice situation, there were instances of preference for the less desirable nutritional choice. Extension of this work to wild animals remains to be completed.

Since the taste bud is a structure common to the higher animals, it is a reasonable starting point in a study of taste. What precisely is the role of these receptors in taste? What is the significance of the number of taste buds to taste? One thinks of taste buds as a key link in the chain of taste reactions. It has been reported that the number of taste buds in humans begins to decrease in late middle age (Mochizuki, 1939) and parallels the decline in ability to taste (Cooper *et al.*, 1959). It should be added that opinion on the relationship of taste acuity to aging is not unanimous (Cohen and Gitman, 1959). The domestic chick (Kare *et al.*, 1957) will totally avoid solutions of chemicals in dilutions almost beyond our perceptive abilities. This rejection can be accomplished with less than a dozen taste buds (Lindenmaier and Kare, 1959). Ruminants with 20,000–25,000 taste buds will tolerate, if not relish, some compounds which are offensive to the chick (Weber, W., R. O. Davies, and M. R. Kare, 1960. Distribution of taste buds and changes with age in the ruminant [unpublished data]). The significance of number of taste buds to taste preference remains to be explained.

A series of experiments was carried out in which groups of chicks were offered a choice of a sugar solution or distilled water (Kare and Medway, 1959). The sugars included the monosaccharides—xylose, arabinose, fructose, glucose, mannose, and galactose; the disaccharides —sucrose, lactose and maltose; and the trisaccharide, raffinose. These sugars were selected with a view to introducing variables such as osmotic pressure, viscosity, optical rotation, reducing ability, density, melting point, configuration, solubility, nutritive value, toxicity, sweetness (as we know it), and others. After several hundred trials with over 2,000 chicks, there was no indication that a specific physical or chemical factor was involved in the selection or rejection of any of the carbohydrates. In fact, if any observation is warranted, it would be that these factors apparently had no influence on taste preference. Lawrence and Ferguson (1959), using a more diverse group of chemical compounds in a study to determine molecular properties responsible for characteristic tastes, found no positive correlations.

A summary of our results suggests that the discrimination is based upon absolute specificity, the absolute specificity one associates with enzymatic activity. An enzyme concept receives support from the fact that stereoisomers will evoke different taste reactions (Lawrence and Ferguson, 1959); however, the enzyme inhibition theory proposed by Baradi and Bourne (1953) has failed to receive any published support. In our own laboratory, the enzymes described by these authors were found only in the deeper layers of the oral mucosa of the chicken (Lindenmaier and Kare, 1959). It would be necessary for a substance to penetrate the epithelium with unusual speed in order to participate in an enzyme reaction under these circumstances. Certainly, further consideration of an enzyme theory appears warranted. Dethier (1956) has summarized the evidence for and against enzyme theories to explain the taste mechanism.

The fowl will discriminate between carbohydrates; while it will accept or is indifferent to glucose or sucrose, it rejects xylose. Figures 1 and 2 illustrate the reaction of the baby chick to sucrose and glucose. Each dot represents the mean preference value

$$\left[\frac{\text{sugar solution consumed}}{\text{total daily fluid intake}} \times 100 \right]$$

for 16 chicks for an 18-day trial. In concentrations from 2.5 to 25.0 per cent (all percentages considered here are weight in volume), all dots are near the 50 per cent line, suggesting a reaction of indifference. It will be noted that the over-all average for both sugars is just over the 50 per cent mark. Perhaps equally noteworthy is the fact that a chick will be indifferent to the thick, viscous syrup of a 25 per cent sugar solution, accepting it about as well as pure water.

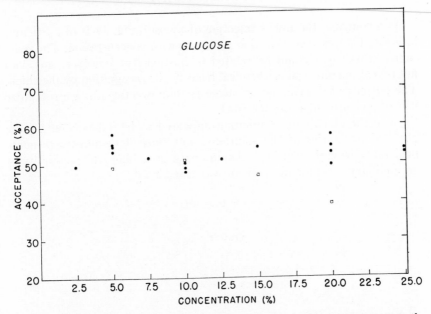

Fig. 1.—Acceptance of increasing concentrations of glucose. Each mark represents the average of the (volume of sugar solution $\times$ 100/total fluid intake) for a pen of 16 chicks during the 18 days after hatching. The alternative choice was distilled water.

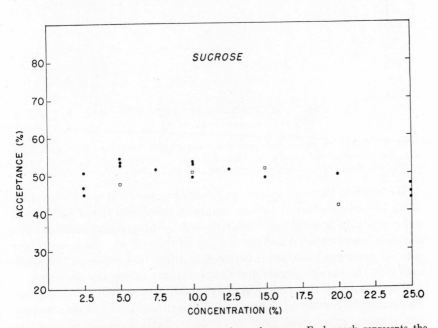

Fig. 2.—Acceptance of increasing concentrations of sucrose. Each mark represents the average of the (volume of sugar solution $\times$ 100/total fluid intake) for a pen of 16 chicks during the 18 days after hatching. The alternative choice was distilled water.

As a contrast, the fowl's rejection of xylose (Fig. 3) is of particular interest. The per cent rejection increases with concentration. The reaction to this sugar could be related to its toxicity; however, this does not reveal the physical or chemical basis for its recognition by the chick. The pattern of discrimination suggests that sweetness as we recognize it is of no consequence to the fowl.

Since the chick's discrimination appeared to be independent of the physical properties of the solutions, and since it demonstrates acute preference behavior with less than a dozen taste buds, the possibility of an auxiliary receptor mechanism was considered.

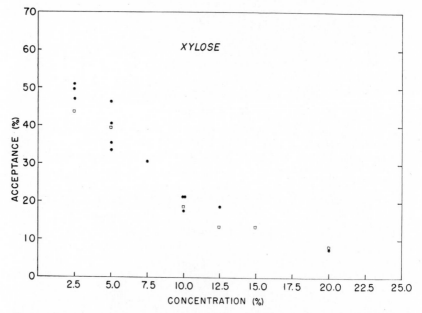

Fig. 3.—Reduced acceptance of increasing concentrations of xylose. Each mark represents the average of the (volume of sugar solution × 100/total fluid intake) for a pen of 16 chicks during the 18 days after hatching. The alternative choice was distilled water.

We applied glucose, xylose, and other sugars to strips of intestine. The contrasting effect of various sugars on villus movement and intestinal activity in general has been reported by Magee and Reid (1931). Motility was measured and the activity of the villi was observed. There was no apparent correlation between motility that followed the application of the various sugars and the preference previously observed.

The possibility that chemical discrimination occurred in the crop was investigated (Soedarmo, Kare, and Wasserman, 1961). Two contrasting sugars—xylose and glucose—were studied. Working *in vivo*, the crop was ligated and the sugars introduced. Glucose was removed but xylose was not. Using C^{14}-labeled sugars, activity was observed in the circulatory system shortly after glucose was introduced into the ligated crop, but not after xylose. Similar radiocarbon studies indicated that both xylose and glucose were immediately removed from the mouth.

Would it be unreasonable to suggest that rejection of xylose does not necessarily involve the taste buds at all? Certainly it is removed rapidly enough from the mouth so that the receptor for the xylose does not have to be in the mouth cavity at all. Materials can be injected intravenously and be tasted. This has been corroborated by many patients who report tasting medicaments administered subcutaneously. The

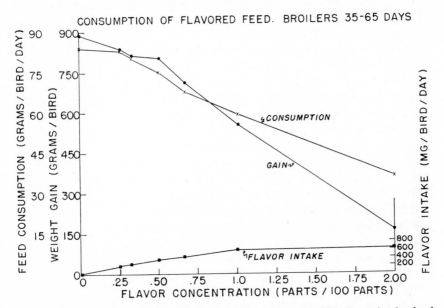

Fig. 4.—An illustration of how taste can influence food intake. With increasing levels of the offensive flavor, total food consumption is reduced. Each *point* represents measurements from at least 1 group of 5 animals for a period of 30 days.

body is really a network of chemoreceptors, e.g., the classical chemoreceptor, the carotid sinus. This suggests a study, with labeled compounds each with a specific taste action, introduced intravenously. Subsequently, autoradiographic studies would be carried out on whole body sections.

The relationship of taste to hunger and appetite or to food intake is not entirely clear. We approached the subject by adding materials which in small quantity were highly offensive to the fowl, and we reduced food intake (Kare and Pick, 1960). With 2 per cent of an anthranilic-acid derivative in the diet, the animal will eat only enough to stay alive; this trial continued over an 18-day period (Fig. 4). A parallel study was carried out in drinking water, and it was found that we could reduce fluid consumption 40 per cent with one-tenth the concentration of the material necessary in the feed. The reduced fluid consumption approached the minimum amount of water necessary for life. A pharmacological action was probably not involved since only one-tenth of the material is required when administered in water, and this quantity can be consumed in feed without apparent ill effect. The minimum amount of this material necessary for the complete avoidance of food or water, where a choice is available, must be increased tenfold in a no-choice situation before there is a reduction in food or water intake. Beginning with the most offensive feed, the intake could be increased by removing offensiveness. These data clearly support the contention that taste can influence food intake.

If chickens are indifferent to the common sugars, what would happen to their food intake if continuously given 10 per cent sucrose in their drinking water? If they are indifferent to the taste of sucrose solutions, will the sucrose solution influence total intake of dry feed? In our laboratory we are now considering the mechanism which the bird uses for regulating its caloric intake.

A study similar to the one described earlier with a variety of sugars has been carried out with calves and pigs. The results suggest that the reactions to sugars of both the calf and pig are different from man's judgment of taste. Sucrose in a 1 per cent solution was significantly preferred to water by calves (Pick and Kare, 1959). This is not the situation with the chick or cat. As data accumulate on the preference of various animals for a variety of chemical entities, it becomes obvious that each species must be considered separately. Unless it is otherwise established, it is reasonable to assume that each species lives in an isolated taste world.

The experiments with large animals were all carried out using measurements of single animals, which has permitted observation of the tremendous individual variation. A good example is the mean value, one of marginal preference by the calf for 1 per cent fructose (Table 1). However, on examining the results for the individual calves, it can be observed that Calf 1 was indifferent to the fructose solution while Calf 5 exhibited a preference for it of at least nine to one over the water.

This situation with calves and fructose is not an isolated incident. We have intensively studied the reaction of pigs to saccharin and have found that some pigs markedly prefer saccharin solutions to water. Some were indifferent, while a sizable minority rejected saccharin solutions at every concentration offered to them. The individual reactions of the members of a single litter are illustrated in Figure 5. A range of response was also observed by the same pigs with quinine sulfate and sucrose solutions. However, there was no correlation between the preference for the various chemical entities. Apparently the response to each of the materials tested was specific for the individual and the chemical entity.

A more extensive study on individual variation in taste response was carried out on chicks by Ficken and Kare (1961). A series of chlorides was included. While the majority of birds actively rejected dilute solutions of ferric chloride, a few animals preferred it to distilled water.

TABLE 1

INDIVIDUAL DIFFERENCES IN PREFERENCE OF CALVES
FOR A 1 PER CENT SOLUTION OF FRUCTOSE*

CALF No.	MEAN PREFERENCE	DAILY PREFERENCE	
		Calf 1	Calf 5
1.............	48.5	36.6	97.8
2.............	70.9	61.4	98.0
3.............	68.2	46.9	95.9
4.............	67.3	92.5	99.4
5.............	97.6	17.5	89.8
6.............	57.6	55.0	98.6
7.............	61.9	64.1	94.3
8.............	53.3	40.3	94.2
9.............	46.9	24.8	98.8
		31.1	99.1

* Preference = (sugar solution consumed / total fluid intake) $\times$ 100.

SACCHARIN SOLUTION CONSUMPTION
expressed as a percentage of total fluid consumption

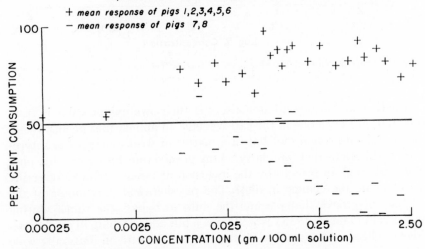

FIG. 5.—This illustrates the differences in reaction to saccharin solution by pigs from a single litter. The measurements represent long-term exposure to the choice between water and the saccharin solution.

Further, the deviant individuals for each chloride were not the same birds. The collective response of all animals studied suggests an underlying continuum in sensitivity.

What are the causes for these differences between individuals? Are they genetic or learned? Have they some nutritional significance, and was there at one time any survival value? We do not know. It is tempting to suggest a genetic basis for the taste differences. If there is, it has been overlooked in domestic animal breeding programs. In humans and rats some basis exists (Blakeslee and Fox, 1932; Nachman, 1959). This thesis is now being evaluated with chicks.

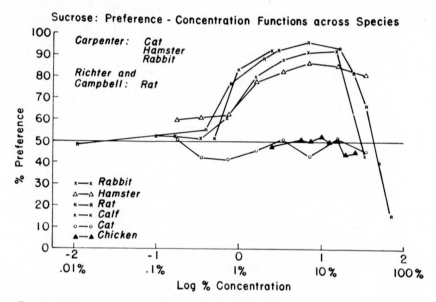

Fig. 6.—Difference in taste response between species. The measurements represent long-term exposure to the choice between water and the sugar solutions.

The calf, and in fact all animals, offer their own unique value in taste research. For example, in the calf we have an animal that begins life on a high animal-protein diet but in a matter of weeks changes to a typically herbivorous diet. Similarly, many graniverous birds start life on a diet made high in protein by the inclusion of insects. Is taste directing or following the change in diet? The physiological functioning of the esophageal groove that permits the milk to bypass the rumen during this period (Dukes, 1955) is well known but adds nothing to our knowledge of changes in taste. Unless the calf is born with an unusually wide taste tolerance, changes probably occur during this period.

If we combine our data with those of Carpenter (Fig. 6), it is apparent that the selection of the specific animal for a taste study can be critical. Further, since individual variation can be so great, taste studies with a small number of subjects must be particularly suspect.

Since animals have unique physiological developments (for example, the chicken's refractiveness to insulin), these might be of particular consequence in a taste study. The translation of results with one species into a general theory is always questionable, but in taste there is an even greater risk, since the responses probably have a pattern peculiar to the species. While caution must be applied for the reasons stated, it is also suggested that the unique taste patterns of species or individuals can be a natural opportunity to explain the mechanisms, just as the inborn errors of metabolism have been a starting point for important metabolic investigations.

The Osmotic Postingestion Factor in the Regulation of Glucose Appetite

Harry L. Jacobs

KARE HAS POINTED OUT (chap. ii, Fig. 6) that if one takes a calf, rat, rabbit, or hamster and gives it a choice of several concentrations of sucrose solution, measuring volume intake or relative preference, the resulting function will have a rapidly rising limb maximizing at about 10 per cent (weight in volume, 0.3M), followed by a slowly declining limb at higher concentrations. As Richter and Campbell (1940) have shown for the rat, this inverted U-shaped function is stable and can be demonstrated for most of the common sugars. I might point out that all of the functions presented in the data discussed by Kare (chap. ii, Fig. 6) were obtained in preference tests where relative intake was measured for at least a 24-hour period. I will refer to this procedure as "long-term" preference testing.

If we now restrict our discussion to data available on the rat, shorten the time the solution is available to the animal or in some way limit the volume intake during ingestion, the resulting preference function is quite different. Under these conditions the relationship between preference and concentration is positive in direction and close to linear (Guttman, 1954; Jacobs, 1960). Although systematic comparisons between species have not been made with the brief-exposure technique, I would strongly suspect that any species showing the inverted-U function in a long-term test would also show a monotonically increasing function in a brief-exposure test.

In summary, we seem to have two kinds of preference for sugar solutions in the rat, depending upon the method of measuring preference. My task will be to outline a physiological theory to account for these data, present the available evidence in favor of it, and then evaluate this approach in the light of recent evidence collected in our laboratory.

Over the last decade a reasonably concise and quite parsimonious physiological explanation for these two preference functions has been developed. The set of arguments that I will present can be attributed primarily to McCleary's well-known paper (McCleary, 1953) on the postingestion factor in glucose appetite. Also important are the early observation and subsequent work by Young and his colleagues (Young, 1949; Young and Greene, 1953), the clear ideas on the effect of osmotic factors on salt preference developed by Stellar (Stellar *et al.*, 1954), and the interpretive papers on this subject by Young (1957) and Pfaffmann (1959*b*).

Let us start with the data presented above and ask why the rat shows the monotonically increasing function when allowed a brief time to drink and then shifts to the inverted-U function when offered unrestricted access to the solutions. The general assumption probably applicable here is that, in a brief-exposure test, peripheral receptor stimulation is determining intake. After swallowing, a host of postingestion factors begin to operate. The concept of a "postingestion" factor logically applies to all physiological events that take place after swallowing. However, since the appearance of McCleary's paper in 1953, the emphasis has been on one particular kind of postingestion factor, the osmotic properties of the solution being ingested. Because it works out so beautifully in the psychological literature, it is often implicitly assumed that postingestion is equivalent to osmotic pressure.

The argument for the operation of the osmotic postingestion factor is very clear. We assume that an organism ingesting a hypertonic solution will become dehydrated because of the osmotic properties of the solution pulling water into the stomach. This will produce a thirsty animal.

The actual site of the dehydration, the specific sequence of events, and the problem of feedback to the hypothalamus to stop the continued ingestion of the hypertonic solution are all problems for the physiologist working in the area of thirst. The critical point for the psychologist is that the ingestion of any hypertonic solution, in this case something tasting sweet and containing calories, dehydrates the animal and makes him thirsty. Thus, the initial response to contact with the solution is determined by taste alone and would ordinarily produce the monotonically increasing preference function. Once drinking starts, however, a simple negative feedback system goes into operation. If the animal continues to drink the hypertonic solution, trying to get maximum sweetness, it will become dehydrated; thus, over a 24-hour period, the animal attempts to maximize taste and minimize dehydration, selecting a solution somewhere around the 10 per cent level as found in most experiments using long-term preference tests.

In summary, this approach uses a simple physical factor, the colligative properties of the ingested solution, to explain the obtained differences in preference at the behavioral level. It is an extremely attractive theory in that it appears to explain long-term appetites for sugars without reference to their metabolic properties.

Let me outline the two major lines of evidence in support of the theory. A few years ago Shuford (1959) performed a series of experiments using food-and-water-satiated rats and a single-bottle intake test, in which he tried various sucrose concentrations until he found three concentrations which respectively produced the same degree of fluid

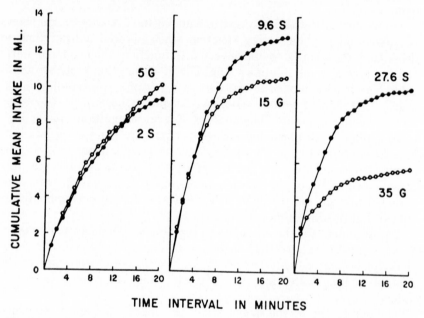

Fig. 7.—Twenty-minute intake of 3 pairs of sugar solutions in single-bottle tests in food-and-water-satiated animals. (Modified from: Shuford, E. 1959. Palatability and osmotic pressure of glucose and sucrose solutions as determinants of intake. Jour. Comp. Physiol. Psychol., **52**:150.)

intake during a 12-minute test as three standard glucose solutions. The three matches were 5 per cent (0.03M) glucose and 2 per cent (0.06M) sucrose, 15 per cent (0.8M) glucose and 9.6 per cent (0.28M) sucrose, and 35 per cent (1.9M) glucose and 27.6 per cent (0.81M) sucrose. However, in a subsequent experiment, he noted that if the test was continued for 20 minutes, two of the above matches no longer held (Fig. 7).

How do we interpret these data? If we assume that the brief-exposure, 12-minute intake is determined by taste alone, another factor must be coming into the picture to regulate rate of approach to satiation during the longer 20-minute test. What could it be?

Figure 8 demonstrates what Shuford thinks this factor might be.

Ignoring the low pair (2 per cent sucrose and 5 per cent glucose), which did not differentiate in the 20-minute test, he plots the cumulative intake curves at four-minute intervals for the two remaining pairs, placing all solutions on the abscissa on the basis of their computed osmotic pressure. In the case of sucrose, it was necessary to compute the pre-hydrolytic osmotic pressure. This last decision leads Shuford to assume (not discussed in the paper) that all of the osmotic effects are taking place at the stomach.

The results are quite clear-cut. After the first minute (where taste alone is presumably operating), the amount drunk is inversely related to the osmotic pressure of the ingested solutions. As expected, the osmotic postingestion effect is greatest in the last part of the 20-minute drinking period.

These data are quite acceptable as indirect evidence for the postingestion osmotic theory outlined above. Although the action of osmotic pressure as an independent variable is inferred, the presumptive evidence is quite good.

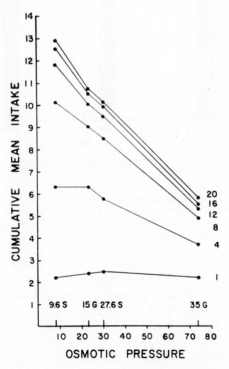

Fig. 8.—Cumulative mean intake (in ml. of solution) of the sucrose (S) and glucose (G) pairs shown in Fig. 7, with the 2S–5G pair excluded, plotted at 1, 4, 8, 12, 16, and 20 minutes of exposure to the solution as a function of osmotic pressure (in atmospheres). (Modified from: Shuford, E. 1959. Palatability and osmotic pressure of glucose and sucrose solutions as determinants of intake. Jour. Comp. Physiol. Psychol., **52**:150.)

The most direct experimental evidence for the osmotic theory was presented by McCleary (1953). This investigator performed a series of experiments in which he measured preference by allowing a one-hour intake test from a single bottle containing water, or a hypotonic, isotonic, or hypertonic glucose solution. Since he wished to have a base line that would maximize intake for the short test period, all animals were deprived of water for 16 hours (Weiner and Stellar, 1951). He measured the effect of intragastric, intraperitoneal, and intravenous

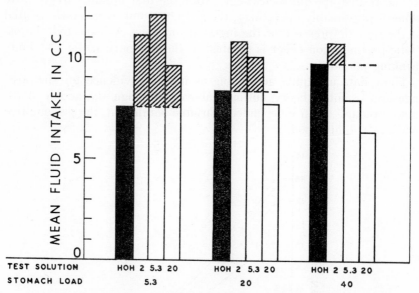

CONCENTRATION OF GLUCOSE SOLUTION IN PERCENT

Fig. 9.—Effect of 3 different concentrations of glucose, used as stomach loads, on the subsequent intake of various concentrations of glucose and water. Water intake is indicated by the black bars while the shaded portions of the bars indicate where the glucose solutions were taken in excess of water. (Reproduced from: McCleary, R. A. 1953. Taste and post-ingestion factors in specific-hunger behavior. Jour. Comp. Physiol. Psychol., 46:411.)

loads on subsequent one-hour glucose or water intake. We will only be concerned with the results of his intragastric loads.

Figure 9 shows the effect of isotonic and hypertonic glucose loads administered by stomach tube on the intake of water, 2 per cent (0.1M), 5.3 per cent (0.3M, isotonic), and hypertonic glucose solution. The results show that load concentration is inversely related to glucose intake and directly related to water intake. The increasing satiety value of highly concentrated glucose loads can be a function of either the osmotic or the metabolic properties of the glucose loads. The fact that water intake was reciprocally related to glucose intake is in agreement with the osmotic hypothesis. It is difficult to see how the metabolic properties of glucose could produce a thirsty animal.

Since the increased water intake is in agreement with the osmotic theory and is not predictable from metabolic effects, McCleary proceeded further. His argument was simple. If the inhibition of glucose intake in Figure 9 was indeed a function of the colligative properties of the glucose load, then the administration of non-metabolizable osmotic loads should have identical effects. Thus, McCleary proceeded to ad-

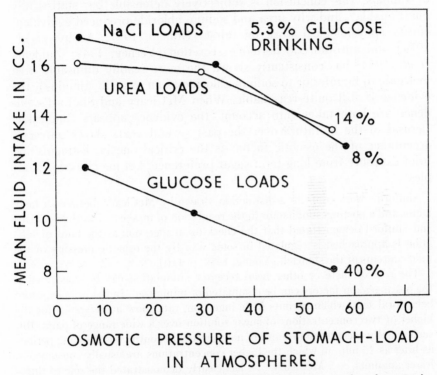

Fig. 10.—Effect of 3 different solutions, used as stomach loads, on the subsequent intake of 5.3 per cent glucose solution. The 3 different concentrations used for each load were approximately matched between loads in terms of osmotic pressure. (Modified from: Mc-Cleary, R. A. 1953. Taste and post-ingestion factors in specific-hunger behavior. Jour. Comp. Physiol. Psychol., **46**:411.)

minister a series of sodium-chloride and urea loads and compared them with the glucose effects discussed above.

Figure 10 shows the results of this series of experiments. McCleary measured only the intake of 5.3 per cent (0.3M, isotonic) glucose. Like Shuford, he plotted volume intake against osmotic pressure. The glucose data on this figure are from the experiment discussed above (Fig. 9).

The data are quite consistent. Increased osmotic loads significantly inhibited glucose intake in all three cases. The slopes of the three curves are quite similar, suggesting that the colligative properties of glucose mediate its satiety value independent of its metabolic properties. Mc-

Cleary performed several other experiments in defense of his thesis, but the data in this figure are the best direct evidence for the operation of osmotic factors in sugar appetite.

Although one wonders why the glucose loads produced consistently less intake at all points (McCleary did not analyze these data on the grounds that the variance was inflated due to the use of separate groups of animals; this conclusion is subjectively defensible but statistically questionable), and why urea and sodium chloride produced equivalent effects (physiological work on thirst [Gilman, 1937; Adolph *et al.*, 1954] and anti-diuretic hormone secretion [Verney, 1947; Zuidema *et al.*, 1956] has consistently shown the more readily diffusable urea molecule to be inferior to sodium chloride as an osmotic stimulus), the evidence is still quite reasonable. When McCleary and Shuford's evidence are both taken into account, the evidence appears conclusive. Perusal of the literature over the past several years shows universal acceptance of the osmotic factor as the critical one in distinguishing brief exposure from long-term sugar preference. Let me cite two examples:

Shuford's work confirms a distinction, drawn by McCleary, between a taste factor and a postingestion factor in the regulation of intake. . . . Both McCleary and Shuford demonstrated that the checking of ingestion as the limit of satiation is approached is regulated in some way by the osmotic pressure of the fluid contents of the stomach [Young, 1959, p. 110].

The role of taste or other head receptor stimulation can be uncovered if the postingestion factors can be eliminated or minimized. In the brief exposure behavioral test, which permits little ingestion, rats show a preference for the higher of two concentrations of sugar solution over a wide range of pairs. But such equally accepted solutions are not ingested in continuous drinking periods as brief as 20 min. in which the higher concentrations are usually consumed in lesser amounts. . . . McCleary . . . has clearly demonstrated the role of intragastric osmotic pressure in this effect [Pfaffmann, 1959*b*, p. 529].

I believe that both of these statements present reasonable interpretations of the work of McCleary and Shuford. Until quite recently, I would have agreed wholeheartedly with these conclusions. Over the past year or so, I have been concerned with an analysis of the peripheral information systems regulating the rate of approach to satiation in glucose appetite. As would be expected from McCleary's work, I have been able, consistently, to inhibit voluntary glucose intake for up to six hours with intragastric loads of hypertonic glucose.

I do not ordinarily use the method of single stimuli in my laboratory; my rats always have two choices between sugar solution and tap water. If osmotic factors are mediating the voluntary inhibition of glucose intake, one would also expect a voluntary increase in water intake in a two-choice test. I have used load volumes as high as 3 per cent body weight (2M) and 2 per cent body weight load (25° C.) concentrations as high as 5.5M (99 per cent) glucose.

I have never found the expected increase in water intake under these conditions (Jacobs, 1960). If the osmotic theory were correct, I should have gotten thirsty animals. Although I was not concerned with amplifying the osmotic theory, it was necessary for me to explain this.

My next step was to design a series of experiments to evaluate the effect of water deprivation on the intragastric load effect. I used 24-hour deprivation, 1 per cent body weight loads, and simplified the situation

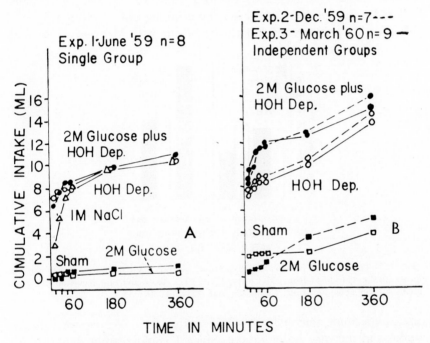

Fig. 11.—The effect of hypertonic glucose loads on the 6-hour water intake in food-and-water-satiated or 24-hour water-deprived rats.

by using a six-hour drinking test with only water available to drink. Figure 11 presents the results of three replications of these experiments. The 2M (36 per cent) glucose load is equivalent to sham tubing, neither raising water intake. As expected, a 1M (6 per cent) sodium chloride load (Fig. 11, A) or 24 hours of the water deprivation (Fig. 11, A and B) produced thirsty animals. The critical result was that the glucose load increased water intake only when paired with water deprivation. The trend in Figure 11, B, for glucose plus water deprivation to increase water intake when compared to water deprivation alone, was not significant. Thus, as I found in the two-choice situation discussed above, glucose loads have no effect on water-satiated rats; however, thirst is produced when glucose loads are paired with water deprivation.

On the basis of these experiments, all of the apparent osmotic effects of glucose can be attributed to water deprivation. At this point I decided to try a direct repetition of the critical parts of McCleary's work with adequate controls to evaluate the effect of his water deprivation base line. I designed a second series of experiments in which I duplicated his procedure with two variations. (1) I continued to use my Holtzman-strain albino rats instead of shifting to the Brown and Hooded Lashley strains used by McCleary. (2) McCleary removed feed and water for two hours after the drinking tests. I did not.

Figure 12 compares my laboratory results with McCleary's. In both

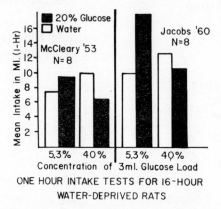

ONE HOUR INTAKE TESTS FOR 16-HOUR
WATER-DEPRIVED RATS

Fig. 12.—The effect of isotonic and hypertonic glucose loads on water and hypertonic glucose intake. (Modified from: McCleary, R. A. 1953. Taste and post-ingestion factors in specific-hunger behavior. Jour. Comp. Physiol. Psychol., **46**:411.)

cases, hypertonic glucose loads significantly ($P = .05$) decrease glucose intake and increase water intake. Since I could readily duplicate his results in my laboratory, it seemed reasonable to conclude that the remaining procedural differences were irrelevant. It should be noted that my animals ingested more than McCleary's under all conditions. In the light of Kare's discussion of comparative preferences, it is quite possible that this is a function of strain differences.

I now went on to the critical experiments, measuring the effect of isotonic (5.3 per cent, 0.3M) and hypertonic (40 per cent, 2.2M) loads of glucose on the subsequent intake of water or hypertonic (20 per cent, 1.1M) glucose in water-satiated (my previous work) or water-deprived (McCleary's procedure) rats. I added water-load and no-load conditions for more precise evaluation of the load effects. The eight conditions were run with latin square control for order effects.

Two groups of eight rats were run, one tested for water intake, the other tested for glucose intake.

Figure 13 shows the results of these experiments. I will discuss the water intake first. In agreement with my first series of experiments, none of the load conditions were significantly different from one another; thus, glucose loads had no thirst effect in water-satiated (*ad libitum*) animals. Let us now examine the intake of the water-deprived animals. If we only look at the glucose-load conditions (as McCleary did), the hypertonic load apparently increases water intake. However, when the no-load (control) and water-load conditions are taken into account, the picture changes dramatically. The average intake under

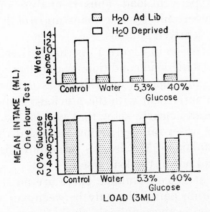

Fig. 13.—The effect of water, isotonic, or hypertonic glucose loads, administered by stomach tube, on the subsequent 1-hour intake of water (*upper graph*) or hypertonic glucose (*lower graph*) in food-and-water-satiated or in 16-hour water-deprived rats using single-bottle drinking tests.

water or isotonic-glucose load was the same, but both of these conditions significantly lowered water intake when compared to the control (no-load) or hypertonic-load condition. Since these animals were already dehydrated, it would be expected that any free water injected by stomach tube would decrease their water deficit proportionately. This is exactly what occurred. If a correction is made for the amount of water administered in the osmotically inert water or isotonic-glucose loads, both mean intakes are raised to within .5 ml. of the other pair and the significant differences disappear. I did not correct for the water content of the hypertonic load for the following reason. If, as McCleary assumes, hypertonic glucose is acting on a colligative basis, its water content would not be free to reduce water-deprivation dehydration already present.

It would seem reasonable to apply the same correction to the water-intake data in McCleary's original experiment. Let us examine Figure 9

again. McCleary found that the water intakes with the 5.3 per cent
(0.3M), 20 per cent (1.1M), and 40 per cent (2.2M) glucose loads were
7.5 ml., 8.25 ml., and 10 ml., respectively (computed from his graph).
The two end points were significantly different, and the trend is
approximately linear. Application of this correction changes the picture
considerably.

The water content of the three ml. load is between 2.83 ml. and 2.84
ml. (The approximation had to be made because McCleary did not
specify his method of computing glucose percentage.) If this is added
to the obtained intake under isotonic-load conditions, the total intake
(load plus voluntary intake) rises to approximately 10.3 ml. which is
equivalent to the 40 per cent load. Thus, re-analysis of McCleary's own
data shows that hypertonic glucose loads apparently do not increase
water intake in the deprived animals.

The critical comparison in Figure 13 is that between the control condition and the hypertonic-load condition. Water deprivation alone (control) produces the same amount of drinking as that produced with the
hypertonic load. In agreement with the previous study on water intake
(Fig. 11), these results clearly show that glucose loads have no thirst
stimulating effect in water-satiated animals and that the apparent effect
in water-deprived animals (McCleary's procedure) is due to deprivation dehydration and not to the load itself.

Now let us look at glucose intake. There are no statistically significant differences within pairs; the only between-pair difference that is
significant is the drop in those animals given 40 per cent glucose loads.
Thus, the only way we can reduce glucose intake is to give the animal a
glucose load; thirst has no effect at all.

In summary, these experiments have shown that water intake is primarily affected by deprivation dehydration. Glucose intake is primarily
affected by the amount of glucose in the load and is not a function of
its osmotic properties. On the basis of this experimental analysis of
McCleary's work, it seems reasonable to conclude that the apparent
osmotic effects demonstrated in his experiments were due to an artifact;
he happened to use water deprivation as his base line. I should add that
McCleary's original conclusions are quite logical and still applicable to
his experiments. My rejection of his conclusion is based upon evidence
not available to him at the time.

Up to this point, all I have really done is to point out that the independent variable in Shuford's work (Fig. 8) and McCleary's work
(Fig. 10) is incorrectly labeled. It is still necessary to substitute a
reasonable alternative to osmotic pressure. I would like to suggest
"calories" as an adequate substitute. Let us take this concept and see
how it fits the data.

Shuford's data (Fig. 8) present the most difficult case. If we substi-

tute "calories" for "osmotic pressure" on his abscissa and compute
calories/100 cc ingested, the four sugars line up in the same order
found by Shuford with calorie values of 38.4, 60, 110, and 140. Although calories can handle the ranking effects, they are not adequate to
explain the detailed shape of Shuford's curves. In both glucose-load
cases, the drop in intake is greater than that which would be expected
on the basis of an assumed linear relation between calories and satiety
value. This suggests a chemical-specific glucose effect, at least in the
sense that calories from glucose have more satiety value than those supplied in the fructose moiety of the sucrose molecule.

The same thing can be done for McCleary's data in Figure 10. Here
the calories/100 cc ingested are 21.2, 40, and 120 for the three glucose
loads used. Comparison of the caloric value with volume ingested again
suggests a non-linear function.

In summary, calories have been suggested as providing adequate
alternate explanations for the data obtained by McCleary and Shuford.
I would not argue that calories may in any way be a final answer. I am
not sure which of many postingestion factors may be critical in the
regulation of glucose intake. I am quite sure that it is not osmotic.
Many of the classical as well as many new ideas developed in work in
the physiology of hunger may well be applicable, specific dynamic action, blood glucose shifts, chemoreceptors in the gastrointestinal tract
as Kare has suggested; some or all of these may be involved. (Recent
data support calories as modulators of glucose intake [Jacobs, 1961].)

DISCUSSION

KITCHELL: What about your pretreatment in your brief exposure?
Pretreatment greatly influences intake in animals like calves, because
they will not pay any attention to their containers.

JACOBS: One of the nice things about working with "sweets" is that you
can depend upon a reasonably stable base-intake level. For example,
you can use saccharin in food-satiated rats and still get quite a bit of
intake. You can show the inverted-U-shaped curve for saccharin, for
example, regardless of the immediate dietary history of the animal.

TITLEBAUM: In the loads you are giving, glucose has calories as well
as osmotic pressure. Why not try something which gives osmotic pressure but not calories? I think this would be a much better test of your
theory. I think a more definitive experiment would use something like
mannitol, which tastes sweet and can give osmotic pressure variability
and yet has no caloric value, for both loads and oral intake. This would
be helpful in terms of your own study, where you are now basing your
theory on caloric values as the variable determining drinking in the test
situation.

JACOBS: The series of experiments I described was designed to evaluate osmotic pressure rather than to gain positive evidence for a caloric theory. I merely used the caloric idea as an acceptable substitute until more data are available. Part of the program of research going on in the laboratory now is essentially to try the kind of thing you suggest. With mannitol you have a difficult time getting equal sweetness, if this is what you are suggesting. I am thinking of working along the lines of independently manipulating sweetness and caloric value, using saccharin as my sweetness equalizer. For example, I might add gum acacia or propylene glycol to saccharin for bulk and osmotic effects, or add saccharin to sweeten corn-syrup solids which supply calories with little sweetness, etc. I agree with you that there is need for further delineation of what I tentatively call caloric; I am just saying that I can add calories and the results roughly fit the data of McCleary and Shuford. This is all I need logically. Now I can worry about the work in my own laboratory.

HALPERN: You would be willing to accept change in skin temperature, as Chambers (1956b) proposed to explain the learning found in his intravenous injection experiments (Chambers, 1956a; Coppock and Chambers, 1954), or perhaps chemoreceptors in gastric mucosa (Iggo, 1957), as physiological mechanisms subserving the behavior you have observed.

SCHEIN: With respect to Kare's paper, I wonder if selective ablations of the dozen taste buds in the chick have been tried. Since there are a very small number of taste buds to deal with, can you selectively eliminate them one by one to see if this changes the preference intake? I might add parenthetically that the question is based on the classical concept that specific areas of the tongue are correlated with each of four primary taste qualities (sweet, sour, salty, bitter), which concept has now been superseded by a matter of intensities.

HALPERN: Thresholds do vary between tongue regions, but there does not seem to be specificity throughout a reasonable intensity range (Patton, 1960).

SCHEIN: I gather that nobody here cares to argue in favor of the classical idea of different taste receptivities in different areas of the tongue. However, I think the first question is still appropriate: Has anything in the way of selective ablation and stimulation of individual taste buds been done in the chicken, especially with reference to specific preferences? How about sectioning of the fibers from small groups of taste buds?

KITCHELL: I think possibly that something caustic could be applied to the area where these taste buds are located, destroying the taste buds themselves. This could be confirmed histologically afterward.

KARE: It would be more logical to section the nerve and eliminate them all. We have not done any sectioning.

SCHEIN: One could also electrocoagulate them just as easily. This has not been done with chickens?

HALPERN: I did a small, exploratory study on glossopharyngeal nerve section in the chicken. The data are very limited, but it did seem that the chickens took rather large quantities of 0.3M (1.8 per cent) sodium chloride after bilateral glossopharyngeal sectioning. When they were shifted from water-water to a water-salt choice, their total fluid intake increased about eightfold, and about 30 per cent of that intake was 0.3M (1.8 per cent) sodium chloride. Kare's unpublished data on sodium chloride preferences in the intact chicken indicate that intake of 0.3M (1.8 per cent) sodium chloride represents less than 10 per cent of total fluid intake.

I have a question about the number of taste buds that Kare mentioned: Are these only on the tongue?

KARE: Yes. We searched the mucosa, the palate, and the entire oral cavity down into the esophagus and were able to find no additional classical structures that we would describe as taste buds. There were dome-shaped groups of round cells with structure suggesting they may have a special function in taste. The numbers quoted are based upon a search of the entire buccal cavity and pharynx (Lindenmaier and Kare, 1959).

SCHEIN: Is it possible that in sectioning the nerve rather than destroying a specific bud you may be cutting pathways for receptors other than those specifically on the tongue and, therefore, defeating the delineation of the function of these particular parts on the tongue?

HALPERN: That is certainly possible. From the whole nerve, at least, one can record responses to thermal, mechanical, and gustatory stimulation of the tongue in the chicken (Halpern and Kare, 1961). Therefore, glossopharyngeal nerve sectioning is not simply a case of eliminating information from chemical stimulation. Also, Kitchell (Kitchell *et al.,* 1959) has reported that he was unable to find trigeminal nerve fibers going into the tongue. Therefore, when the glossopharyngeal nerve is sectioned, all tongue sensory innervation is probably eliminated.

KITCHELL: There are many branches of the glossopharyngeal nerve. You would have to get up rather close to the cranial cavity to be central to them, and you might have some interference with the glossal movements of the pharynx.

HALPERN: I sectioned rather close to the brain, not too far from the point where the glossopharyngeal nerve and the vagus nerve, which run together after they leave the skull, separate into two clearly distinguishable nerves. Some of the birds did seem to have some difficulty in swallowing for a little while, but most of them recovered. The data are tentative but do suggest that there might have been a rather radical change in their rejection of high concentrations of sodium chloride.

FISHMAN: I would suggest that colchicine might be a possibility here, assuming a high turnover rate in chickens as in some of the lower mammals. The colchicine apparently decreases the metabolism to such an extent that the turnover is blocked, and within ten to twenty hours there are no taste buds visible (Beidler *et al.*, 1960). This might be a possibility.

SCHEIN: Have you been able to pick up action potentials from single fibers in the glossopharyngeal nerve from specific buds?

KITCHELL: I recorded the thermal responses from single fibers (Kitchell *et al.*, 1959). I recorded some small-fiber responses from the lingual nerve, from which you can observe the single action potentials but not as "single fibers" as such. It is quite difficult, anatomically, to isolate single fibers in the glossopharyngeal nerve of the chicken or mammals because there is apparently interlacing or intermingling of the fasciculi or the fibers, since this is a long nerve. On the other hand, the chorda tympani is an ideal nerve because it has seemingly been "stretched" during growth processes so that the fibers are all running parallel with one another. It makes single-fiber work much easier there than in the glossopharyngeal.

SCHEIN: I think we are satisfied on that particular point. Another question that occurred to me as Kare was speaking was the effect of age, the ontogeny of taste behavior. Is there any evidence that there are specific differential taste preferences? Kare pointed out that the cat and the chicken showed no preferences for sucrose while Jacobs and Scott (1957) reported that chickens had a definite preference for sucrose. Might an age difference amount for the discrepancy in the results? Do either of you care to comment on this point?

JACOBS: As far as explaining differences between laboratories, all I can do at this time is to list the differences between our experiments. First is the factor of age. Kare worked with chicks less than three weeks of age. Second, a more important difference might be that Kare changed waterers every four hours in a random manner in order to avoid position habits. I left them for 24 hours. A third point should be mentioned: I noticed a different kind of drinking behavior than I had ever seen before. Ordinarily, a chicken works by gravity feed, bending down once and then coming up to "swallow." I did not attempt to quantify this, but I noticed that quite often the birds would dip their beaks into the fluid 15 to 20 times before coming up to drink, so that my intake curves were contaminated by "playing in the water." Whether this was due to stickiness, viscosity, or another factor is unknown to me. Thus, what I am labeling "preference" may well not be a function of taste per se.

KITCHELL: If we examine Kare's first paper (Kare *et al.*, 1957), we find that he indicated a slight preference which led me astray in my paper (Kitchell *et al.*, 1959) also. In the second paper (Kare and Medway, 1959) he definitely says that there is no preference for sucrose.

JACOBS: Engelmann's early work (1937) also suggests a preference. I think that further methodological work should be done to standardize and evaluate methods of preference testing with the chicken.

KARE: Since the work you refer to (Kare *et al.*, 1957), in which several trials with sucrose were included among many other types of compounds, we have published a paper entirely devoted to discrimination between carbohydrates by the fowl (Kare and Medway, 1959). In this instance over one hundred trials using some 1,700 chicks were used to determine the preferences for various sugars. The diets were nutritionally adequate. The pattern of discrimination suggested that sweetness as we recognize it is of no consequence to the chick. Viscosity, osmotic pressure, as well as a number of other physical and chemical characteristics, were ruled out as being of consequence in the reaction of the chick to the sugars. (Data which have become available in this laboratory subsequent to this meeting suggest that the nature of the diet can influence the chick's preference for sugar [Kare, Halpern, and Jones, 1961].)

Further, Pick and I have completed but not published as yet a study on methods of preference testing with the chicken. These results would answer many of the questions raised as to the possible role of method.

In relation to sugars, the question of purity poses a problem. Our erratic results with maltose were probably related to dextrins or other minute contaminants.

FISHMAN: I am not familiar with chickens, so I shall have to ask this just for my own information. What is the comparative difference in age between an 18-day-old chicken and a five-day-old rat; a ten-week-old chicken and an adult rat?

KARE: In terms of sexual maturity the rat ages twice as fast; that is, the two- to three-month-old rat is roughly equivalent to the five- or six-month-old chicken. Contradicting this relationship is the over-all physical maturity of a ten-day-old chick, which substantially exceeds that of the five-day-old rat. Further, one cannot assume that there is a parallel development of all the systems in a particular animal. Although one might compare animals on the basis of "old" or "sexually immature" and so forth, a precise conversion of an 18-day-old chick into the equivalent age of a rat would be questionable.

FISHMAN: I asked the question because apparently Beidler is now doing some work with age studies in rat response. I believe he has not been able to get a response from a rat younger than five days. I wonder how this compares in age with a chick at 18 days.

KARE: The three-month-old chicken has two or three dozen taste buds. The day-old has less; apparently the maximum number of buds is acquired some time after hatching. This is analogous, I believe, to the situation in rats. There are no taste buds in the rat until the ninth day post-partum, the maximum being reached at 12 weeks (Torrey, 1940). In humans, on the other hand, the maximum number is found in five- to seven-month fetuses (Arey, 1954).

HALPERN: An experiment done by Pfaffmann some years ago indicated that cats can discriminate between plain milk and milk with sodium chloride added within 18 hours after birth (Pfaffmann, 1936).

TITLEBAUM: Guinea pigs are very well developed at birth, with a full complement of taste buds. In two-choice preference tests, "bitter" substances are rejected by neonate guinea pigs (Fleisher, 1956).

MORRISON: Is there any indication of what was the within-group variance in the groups of 16 chicks shown on Kare's Figures 1 and 2? What I mean is, are there wide strain-differences or, for any reason, similarities within those 16?

KARE: Yes. There is a marked variation which is quite interesting. We found something that we called taste blindness in chickens. One chick will totally contradict the taste response to a specific material of all the others, although no precise experiment has been completed with chicks; all intermediate degrees of response can be expected (Ficken and Kare, 1961).

In an unreported experiment at the New York State game farm, where we were dealing with several thousand pheasants, we observed a few birds that would continue to eat a sprayed feed rejected by other birds. We had been testing the repellent quality of various materials by applying them to the feed.

FROMMER: Speaking of differences in strains, there are some interesting preliminary results from the Brown Psychophysiology Laboratory on recording neural activity from the chorda tympani of rats in response to three different sugars applied to the tongue. Hagstrom and Pfaffmann (1959) have published curves on the chorda tympani nerve response in Wistar rats which show that the summated magnitude of response for sucrose is greater than that for glucose, which is greater than that for maltose, all at equimolar concentrations. New data from Sprague-Dawley rats show that on the secondary rise in the summated response, magnitude of response for glucose is greater than for sucrose. Whether this signifies more than a difference in the way the response magnitudes were measured has yet to be ascertained.

JACOBS: This is interesting in the light of Nachman's recent paper (1959) on the inheritance of saccharin preference. Essentially, he found the same phenomenon that Kare observed in pigs, namely, that some like saccharin and some do not. In the F_1 generation Nachman found a clear-cut difference. He calls it "genetic." It may turn out to be familial. In any event, work such as Frommer described may ultimately explain the physiological basis for this kind of thing.

FISHMAN: Which one of the two strains gave a significant response to sucrose? Were either one of them a good response compared to sodium chloride response in man?

FROMMER: In the Wistar strain the sucrose responses at 1.0M (34 per cent) concentration are below the response to 0.01M (0.055 per cent) sodium chloride.

FISHMAN: The reason I ask is that I habitually use the Wistar strain, and I find they show a very low response to sucrose. Therefore, when I want to try a sucrose experiment, I do not use this strain.

KITCHELL: In Stockholm we used approximately 18 common alley pigeons in our work (Kitchell *et al.*, 1959). In 50 per cent of those, we found a response to saccharin, and in 50 per cent we did not. We repeatedly checked these to find out if this was a technical error, and it was not. I will present these data later for discussion purposes. This may be the explanation of taste-input blindness. There may be behavioral factors which are responsible for the failure of these animals to recognize this as an obnoxious substance. I would like to discriminate between the two.

SCHEIN: This leads to another question—Can taste preferences be modified markedly by learning? Are taste preferences basically innate?

TITLEBAUM: There is a recent experiment on guinea pigs by Warren and Pfaffmann (1959). For the first month of life after being separated from the mother, baby guinea pigs were fed saturated aqueous solutions of sucrose octa-acetate, an extremely bitter substance for humans. They were tested immediately thereafter with sucrose octa-acetate (SOA)– flavored water vs. plain water, and then allowed to mature for about three months on a regular laboratory diet with no access to SOA-flavored food or water. In the initial test there was no difference between the preference for water and for the SOA-flavored water. But when the animals became older, they exhibited the classical dislike of SOA-flavored water. It was clear that the preference was modified initially because control guinea pigs which had not been raised on SOA-flavored water would not drink any SOA water at all, whereas the ones who had been raised on it showed no immediate rejection. In later life both groups of guinea pigs—those who had had early experience with

SOA and those who had not—rejected the SOA solutions when they were paired with tap water in preference tests.

JACOBS: I believe that the question of learning has to be separated into two parts: the classical ontogenetic question and the one asking whether learning can modify intake later in life. There is quite a bit of evidence, a lot from Young's laboratory, that previous dietary history can influence preference. This is related to the latter problem.

HALPERN: An experiment similar to the one which Titlebaum described was reported at the 1960 Eastern Psychological Association meeting (Brush and Amitin, 1960). Quinine hydrochloride was fed to lactating rats and transmitted to the pups through the milk. The experimenters ran into trouble in that many of the pups would not take the milk and died of dehydration. Three per mother survived. Significant temporary changes in quinine preference were observed. At first it appeared that a sustained change had occurred, but a replication with a larger number of rats (seven experimental, six control) indicated that the groups differed significantly only on day 1 (day 21 of life) of testing. These data more or less follow along the lines of the previously described effect of SOA: a short-term difference. In terms of total behavioral effect on the older or more experienced animal, it did not seem to have permanently changed two-bottle preference. (Recent data indicate that preference for low concentrations of DL-methionine is markedly changed by prior exposure to high concentrations [Halpern *et al.*, 1961].)

MORRISON: The results would seem to be compounded, in that it might have been that the animals who had no innate aversion were the ones who survived.

HALPERN: True. However, since the rejection thresholds of the older animals were not different from the controls, that complication might not be too crucial.

SCHEIN: You are dealing with innate here in the individual sense, rather than in the species.

MORRISON: Yes. I assume there is experimental variation in litter mates.

HALPERN: We have unpublished data which show that of twenty Carworth albino rats (not selected as litter mates) offered a choice between 0.0002M (0.015 per cent) quinine sulphate and distilled water for seven consecutive days, only one rat, on only one day, took in more than 11 per cent of the quinine sulphate. That is, of the 140 measurements, only one varied widely from the others.

MORRISON: What kind of concentration would you get in the milk?

HALPERN: I do not know what the concentration in the milk was quantitatively. A fluorescence technique was used to measure it. The mothers were fed 0.0028M (0.1 per cent) quinine hydrochloride mixed with sucrose (Brush and Amitin, 1960).

CARPENTER: I ran experiments with rats by two methods, one that would give long-term results, as Jacobs presented, and another that gives the short-term results he described. Then I reversed the two groups and the long-term results persisted when they became short-term animals, and short-term animals produced the long-term results, so there is some effect of learning. Is that clear? I do not have any explanation for it.

KITCHELL: Relative to Kare's pointing out individual differences between these calves, Bell and Williams (1959) have run some threshold values on monozygotic twin calves at two dissimilar environments, two different herdsmen, and two different total-feeding environments, and they found that both thresholds were quite the same, and the intake was quite the same when they graphed it.

KARE: The only thing I am worried about in Bell's work is the short period of his trials. He ran them for two days. We find that it takes five or six days for a group of calves to learn that they have two choices, that the choices may be in different positions, and that they like one better than the other. In looking back over our data, the first six days are of limited value in many animals. Since Bell's trials were always just two days, I do not know how to interpret his work.

KITCHELL: I did not participate in this work, I just observed it; his differences were real.

HALPERN: The curves that Bell published in *Nature* (Bell and Williams, 1959) showed considerable variability between the individuals of a monozygotic twin-set.

KARE: I would direct a question to Carpenter. When you ran your work, your comparative studies (Carpenter, 1956), from which we used the data on Figure 6, you found that when you offered a cat 7 per cent (0.2M) to 17 per cent (0.5M) sucrose, the cats increased their fluid consumption 200 per cent to 300 per cent. When we give a calf 1 per cent (0.03M) sucrose, it increases its fluid consumption about 100 per cent. In a chicken on an adequate diet, when we give it a sucrose solution, it does not increase its fluid consumption (Kare and Medway, 1959). Perhaps you could explain why, between these species, there is such a substantial alteration in fluid intake when they are offered sucrose. I would assume that the cat and the chicken receive no pleasure from that sugar but that the calf does. But, on the other hand, they divide up in a different fashion as to how they adjust to water intake.

CARPENTER: My published report (Carpenter, 1956) was the second observation of this type. Every time I pick up that paper and look at it I have to remember that I obtained the same result previously under the same conditions in the preliminary testing. I have a couple of cats and they like sweets. I have no explanation that I can think of for this peculiar thing except that the cats probably got sick, vomited, and dehydrated themselves, then drank more and more. Since they could not detect the difference between the sucrose and the water, they went back and drank indiscriminately, made themselves sicker and sicker, and drank more and more water until one of them died. I remember the experiment ended at that point because of the illness of the animals.

SCHEIN: With reference to the graph (Fig. 4), can we expect that by manipulating the taste we can directly manipulate intake both positively and negatively?

KARE: If one removes the offensiveness from the diet, food intake will increase. There is a zone where alterations in taste will not affect intake.

SCHEIN: Can you go above the zero point?

KARE: Tepperman assured me that he could not see why an animal could not consume 25 per cent additional feed or even more; he did not feel the intestine would be a bottleneck. Is that correct? We have been testing his thesis with some decorticated birds. We feed them with a syringe and are limited only by physical capacity of the crop.

TEPPERMAN: The intestine certainly is not a bottleneck because when you put hypothalamic lesions in rats, particularly, or if you give mice a hypothalamic lesion chemically with gold thioglucose, they can very easily double their food intake or even go higher than that. This represents a very complicated series of adaptations, probably initially adaptations in the gastrointestinal tract itself. A whole chain of things happens.

SCHEIN: Are these hypothalamic-lesioned animals indiscriminate feeders? Do they eat voraciously of anything?

TEPPERMAN: Brobeck and I tried some food-choice experiments on lesioned animals about 20 years ago (Brobeck *et al.*, 1943). We fed them cafeteria style and discovered that they had variable preferences, but when we added up the total number of calories, we found that the operated animals uniformly ate massively compared with the controls— two to three times as much in the acute phase of the immediate postoperative period. After a while, after this dynamic phase of the obesity, they go into a kind of static phase in which food intake levels off only moderately above the normal level.

SCHEIN: During the dynamic phase is there any indication of a change in their preferences or a broadening of the variety of food that they will take?

TEPPERMAN: We have not studied this in detail, but Gordon Kennedy at Cambridge in England has been very interested in this business of testing discrimination by lesioned animals, and he thinks that they lose discrimination with the hypothalamic lesions (Kennedy, 1950).

TITLEBAUM: In the experiments reported by Philip Teitelbaum (1955), hypothalamic-lesioned animals were fed food which had been mixed with quinine. The hypothalamic hyperphagic animals would not accept it, while normal rats continued to eat the adulterated food. Their discriminatory behavior was, in fact, more acute than that of normal animals. Anything different from normal conditions disrupts the hypothalamic hyperphagic rat. Increasing the amount of work necessary to receive food reinforcement results in decreased work from a lesioned rat and consequently less food reward. For example, in a bar-press situation in which few presses are required to obtain a food pellet, the hypothalamic hyperphagic rat presses more, and obtains and eats more pellets, than the normal. When many bar-presses are required for each pellet, however, the lesioned rats press less and receive fewer pellets than normals (Miller *et al.*, 1950).

TEPPERMAN: Gordon Kennedy found the same thing. This is a paradox in animals that looked extremely hungry but yet were not willing to exert themselves very much to eat. The experiments that Kennedy did on this were a little complicated because he had an adulterant which is a non-digestible fiber. What he was looking for was an increase in total caloric intake in a diluted diet. After a while you get to the point where the animal just physically cannot take it any more. It was taken from the base line pretty much.

JACOBS: One of the interesting points about that series involves Kennedy's diluting the diets during the dynamic phase. The hyperphagics would respond calorically like a normal rat. Static hyperphagics took about four weeks to respond to a 50 per cent solution with kaolin. In terms of Kare's original comment, Adolph's (Adolph, 1947) dilution experiments with normal rats also show that you can double or triple intake by cutting down available caloric density at least 50 per cent, by adding kaolin or cellulose to some substance.

TEPPERMAN: Lactating animals and very rapidly growing animals, of course, have enormous food intakes relative to their body mass as compared with adult plateau groups, so here again is an example of a physiological situation in which the intake is very high.

HALE: Perhaps I might interject a question aimed at those who know something about neural circuits or electrical circuits. Does the limited number of taste buds in the chicken provide a neural specificity rather than a coding, which might be related to large numbers of taste buds, that is, an analyzer system which permits some ordering of information by coding?

KARE: We ran several dozen compounds in a homologous series and observed there was no orderly discrimination. The chicks differentiated between them from marked preference to marked rejection as we took away a methyl group or added a carboxyl group. They seemed to have the sensitivity to small chemical changes that we have. As in humans no chemical continuity was observed in this and other experiments which would guide a prediction in taste reaction.

BENJAMIN: In relation to the question of the number of taste buds for preference behavior, Pfaffmann did an experiment quite a while ago in which he cut both the IXth and the chorda tympani nerves and thereby reduced the taste buds in the rat's mouth to about 10 per cent of their normal total (Pfaffmann, 1952). Preference for sodium chloride and aversion for quinine were not completely lost. Thresholds went up somewhat, but relatively little compared to the reduction in the number of taste buds. These data indicate that even in the "higher" animal very few taste buds are necessary for some sort of response.

KARE: It may be that we cannot freely go from one species to another when taste is involved as a variable as we can with, say, the circulatory system. If we did an experiment where taste was involved, as in diabetes, the cat apparently reacts differently to sugars than does the rat. It would be difficult to do it with chickens since their regulation of sugar is so unique. Perhaps we have been too free in applying information on taste from one species to another. It would be difficult to interpret any animal taste work in terms of humans.

It would appear that the favorite animal of the psychologist is the rat, and most of them work with white rats. Does not this seem a peculiar animal for taste research? There is an anecdotal reference that pigment is needed to be able to taste; white pigs are not found in parts of Virginia because they eat herbs that are poisonous for them (Moncrieff, 1951), and in some parts of Spain white sheep are not raised because they will eat lethal herbage. Albinos supposedly have a limited ability to taste, and they have a reduced ability to smell. (Recent data indicate that albino rats do not differ from pigmented rats in olfactory ability [Moulton, 1960].)

SCHEIN: Do you use white Leghorns?

KARE: As a matter of fact, in the first work we did, we were able to get white Leghorns free, because the males are of no value commercially. After the first few experiments we discarded them because we held the impression that a pigmented bird appeared to have a more acute sense of taste. Therefore, I wonder why all this valuable psychological work is being done on a white rat?

SCHEIN: Not all the work has been done on white rats. McCleary's results are on pigmented rats and so are Richter's. Jacobs, what kind of rats did you use?

JACOBS: Holtzman albinos.

CHAPTER 3

Neural Response Patterns in Taste

Ralph L. Kitchell

I WILL FIRST just list how neural responses may differ from each other as they are monitored in the nerve coming from the peripheral receptor field. This is in the initial axon or, as we anatomists prefer to call it, the initial dendrite.

Neural responses may differ from each other because of the frequency of the firing of individual fibers. Within a group of individual fibers, there may be changes caused by the individual frequency of firing. For example, the frequency of firing in one fiber may change from five per second up to 20 per second. In addition, the frequency may also change because of the number of fibers firing. Instead of one fiber firing there may be ten fibers firing in response to a substance. We also must consider the effects of the differences in the amplitudes of the action potentials of the different fibers on the neural responses, since the amplitude varies in different-sized fibers. The chorda tympani nerve contains a number of fibers of different sizes, and this undoubtedly has some influence on the neural response. We have done some work on the fiber populations of the chorda tympani of various animals. To date we have finished our studies on the cat, the dog, the pig, and the sheep. We are completing work on the horse, the cow, and the goat. The cat chorda tympani has approximately 1,400 fibers, the dog has 2,000, the pig 4,300, the sheep 4,700. In the cat the greatest number of fibers are from four to six microns in diameter. In other animals it is six to eight microns. It has been shown by others using different nerves that the larger the animal, the larger is the diameter of the fibers.

Also, differences in total neural responses may be observed which are caused by the differences in the rate of rise of the frequency response. In other words, when the stimulus substance is applied to the tongue, there is a rate of change, and this rate of change may vary in response to different substances. This initial response may be called a "phasic" response. We also have to consider the rate of adaptation while the substance remains in contact with the receptors. This may be termed a "static" response. We also can observe differences in duration of response after the stimulus has been removed, the so-called "after-discharge." Some fibers may continue to fire for long periods of time, even after a thorough rinsing of the tongue.

How do we quantify these neural responses? This, I think, has considerable importance if we are to make comparative observations and interpret each other's data. We can record neural responses by direct recording techniques using the cathode-ray oscilloscope. We can visually observe them, we can hear them, we can record them on photographic paper and observe them, we can—if they are individual fiber patterns—count them by just counting the number of action potentials. We also have available to us electronic integrators and events-per-unit-time counting devices. These instruments are extremely useful. The electronic integrator has been used by Beidler and his associates and by other workers for a long time, and much valuable information has been gained from this device. It is important to realize just what it does and what some of its limitations are. The electronic integrator (summator) simply integrates in time all the activities that are being picked up by the electrodes which are in contact with the nerve or the nerve fibers. The output of an integrator will vary according to the three features mentioned earlier: It will vary as the frequency of the potentials in the individual fibers varies, as the number of active fibers varies, and as the magnitudes of the individual action potentials vary. There are unlimited possibilities of combinations of these three variables because the frequency can vary over a wide range, the size of the fibers, as we mentioned, varies over a wide range, and the amplitude can also vary over a wide range. By studying the output of the integrator alone, we cannot distinguish between a group of fibers transmitting at a certain frequency and a smaller number of fibers transmitting at a higher frequency. Second, a group of fibers transmitting at a given frequency with a high amplitude of individual action potentials cannot be distinguished from a large number of fibers transmitting at the same frequency with small amplitude. In recording from a whole nerve or a single fiber, it is important that the variables which may be present, such as the methods used in dissecting the nerve, the method of handling the nerve, and the methods of removal of the connective tissues from the nerve, be as standardized as possible. Variation in these techniques will change the resistance and capacitance between the recording electrodes. The type of recording electrodes and their placement on the nerve will also change the electrical signal which is recorded. We must also direct attention to whether or not we are recording monophasically or diphasically, for this will also affect the integrated response.

In addition to considering the variables due to methods of recording, we also must control the variables as to the method of applying the test solutions to be used. The methods that are used most often are: (1) the flow chamber method of Beidler; (2) the dispensing-burette type of unit as developed by Zotterman; (3) the application of solution by a medicine dropper or a bulb syringe; (4) the application of the solution by using a brush. Each of these has certain limitations and will undoubtedly influence the final result. In all these methods it is important to keep the area of application a constant size. The area of application must be kept the same between animals and within the same animal, for there is undoubtedly anatomical localization of the taste buds. In some animals, as will be mentioned later, it is necessary to move the vallate papillae mechanically in order that the taste solution reach the taste buds: this is another variable. In some animals it is important that the temperature of the tongue be kept very close to the temperature of the solution which is applied: if it is not, this will result in a temperature response which will influence the directly recorded or integrated response. In addition, attention must be directed to the solvents in which we dissolve the solute that we wish to test. In some animals, the solvent itself will give a response. This is the so-called "water response" that Zotterman (1949, 1956) has described and which has been found to exist in the frog, the dog, the cat, the pig, the chicken, the pigeon, and the monkey.

We must also direct our attention to the pre-stimulus treatment applied to the tongue. In instances where there is a response to the solvent, whether it be Ringer's or another, it is often necessary, before the application of the test stimulus, to rinse the tongue with a solution to reduce the spontaneous activity recorded from the nerve. One can adapt the receptors in the tongue to Ringer's solution in many of the animals which have been investigated. It is more difficult to adapt their response to distilled water. We must also recognize that certain of the substances which we apply, such as quinine and acids, will often leave a residual effect: They will depress the neural response for a period of time after application. In most of our experiments, quinine and acids are applied at the last; otherwise, the tongue must be rinsed repeatedly, and often there is a wait for the receptors to recover.

I would like to illustrate some of the neural responses which have been observed. Figure 1 illustrates a neural response obtained from a small branch of the lingual nerve of the chicken (Kitchell *et al.*, 1959). In this experiment the tongue had been flushed with Ringer's solution prior to the application of these solutions. Half-molar (3 per cent) sodium chloride produced a response with the action potentials barely appearing above the noise level. When distilled water was applied, much larger action potentials could be observed. Fifteen per cent (1.7M) glycerine in Ringer's solution resulted in small action potentials; had we applied the glycerine in distilled water both the small and the large action potentials would have appeared. The large potentials would have been directly associated with the different solvent. Two-hundredths molar (7 per cent) quinine produced a small potential response, and 15 per cent (0.46M) sucrose and 0.06 per cent (0.003M) saccharin produced little if any response.

In Figure 2 the response of a small strand of monkey chorda tympani nerve to the application to the tongue of various solutions is illustrated. The downward deflection of the marking signal indicated when the stopcock on the burette was turned. The burette was filled with the solution to the tip. After a very short interval the solution flowed over the tongue. We kept the amount of solution in the burette constant, usually 5 ml. The solution flowed over the tongue for approximately

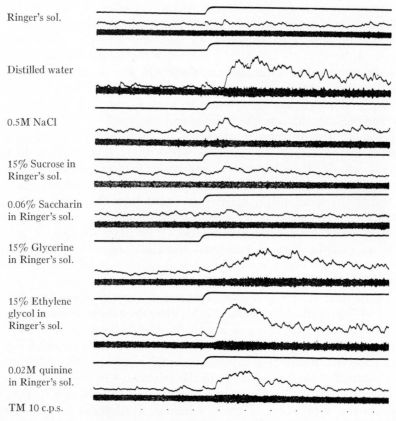

Ringer's sol.

Distilled water

0.5M NaCl

15% Sucrose in
Ringer's sol.

0.06% Saccharin
in Ringer's sol.

15% Glycerine
in Ringer's sol.

15% Ethylene
glycol in
Ringer's sol.

0.02M quinine
in Ringer's sol.

TM 10 c.p.s.

Fig. 1.—Records from the chicken's lingual nerve during application of different solutions to the tongue. In each are recorded, from top to bottom: the signal from the dispensing burette (upward deflection indicates release of the solution), the integrated response, and the direct spike response. Time marks, 1 cps. (Reprinted from: Kitchell, R. L., L. Strom, and Y. Zotterman. 1959. Electrophysiological studies of thermal and taste reception in chickens and pigeons. Acta Physiol. Scand., **46**:133.)

three seconds. In this instance we found responses to substances which taste sweet to humans. There was no response to sodium chloride, but to acetic acid there was a large response; larger action potentials appeared than had occurred for the other three (Gordon *et al.*, 1959).

The next illustration (Fig. 3) is taken from the work of Appelberg (1958) in which he discovered that movement of the vallate papillae on the surface of the cat's tongue resulted in an enhancement of the response. The large spikes which are shown resulted from the stroking of the papillae.

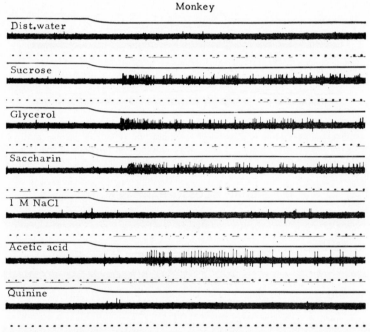

Fig. 2.—Records from a strand of the chorda tympani of *Macacus rhesus* containing a few fibers responding to the application of solution to the tongue. All solutions made up in distilled water. A signal shows the moment of application. Time: 10 per sec. (Modified from: Gordon, G., R. Kitchell, L. Strom, and Y. Zotterman. 1959. The response pattern of taste fibres in the chorda tympani of the monkey. Acta Physiol. Scand., **46**:119.)

In the goat the application of water simultaneously with stroking of the tongue does not produce a response other than that due to stroking the tongue (Fig. 4). A response appears following the application of sodium chloride, quinine, sucrose, acetic acid, and sodium bicarbonate while stroking the tongue. We did not have an integrator available to us during this study, so we were unable to show the integrator response. In this instance, if we did not stroke the vallate papillae we had great difficulty observing any neural response at all in the glossopharyngeal nerve (Baldwin *et al.*, 1959).

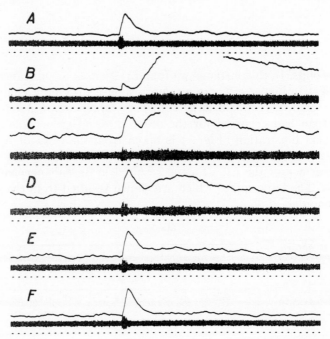

FIG. 3.—Response of the cat's glossopharyngeal nerve to touch on an ipsilateral circumvallate papilla, before (*A*) and after (*C–F*) application of 0.02M quinine hydrochloride solution to the tongue (*B*). Time 0.1 sec. (Reproduced from: Appelberg, B. 1958. Species differences in the taste qualities mediated through the glossopharyngeal nerve. Acta Physiol. Scand., **44**:129.)

GOAT GLOSSOPHARYNGEAL N.

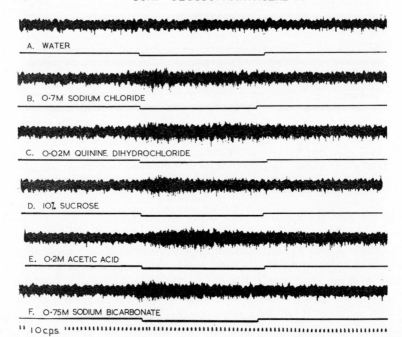

FIG. 4.—Responses evoked from the whole glossopharyngeal nerve of the goat. In each record the time of application of the solution is indicated by the signal. In each instance the circumvallate papillae were gently moved by means of a glass rod. (Bell, F. R., and R. L. Kitchell [unpublished data].)

The "water response" in the pigeon (Kitchell *et al.*, 1959) is illustrated in Figure 5. The application of 0.5M (3 per cent) sodium chloride gave a phasic response with rapid adaptation and little continuing activity; 0.1M (0.55 per cent) sodium chloride, no response; 0.05M (0.3 per cent) and 0.005M (0.03 per cent) sodium chloride, a response of different character than that of the stronger salt in that there was a slower rise in intensity of the response, slower adaptation, and some late responses. This was very similar to the response observed following the application of distilled water.

In the monkey (Gordon *et al.*, 1959), there was a response to the application of Ringer's solution. Distilled water after Ringer's produced a large sustained response, while Ringer's solution followed distilled water produced a phasic type of response. Sodium chloride produced a response of long duration. Sucrose in water produced a response of greater magnitude than did sucrose in Ringer's solution. This again indicates the influence of the solvent on the neural response, in

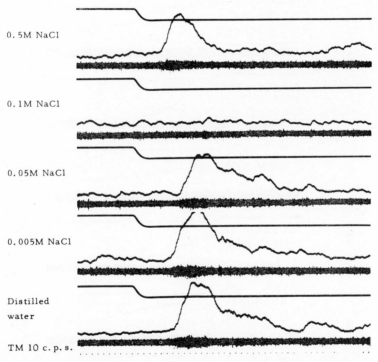

FIG. 5.—Records from the pigeon's lingual nerve during application of NaCl solutions of different concentrations to the tongue. In each are recorded, from top to bottom: the signal from the dispensing burette (downward deflection indicates release of the solution), the integrated response, and the direct spike response. Time marks, 10 cps. (Reprinted from: Kitchell, R. L., L. Strom, and Y. Zotterman. 1959. Electrophysiological studies of thermal and taste reception in chickens and pigeons. Acta Physiol. Scand., **46**:133.)

that there occurred in the receptor and in the nerve fiber a response to the solvent (Fig. 6).

In the next illustration (Fig. 7) responses were recorded from the chorda tympani of anesthetized human beings (Zotterman and Diamant, 1959). It is interesting that in both instances the integrator response went down following the application of distilled water to the tongue. This is similar to what Zotterman has found in the rat (Zotterman, 1956).

The next illustration (Fig. 8) demonstrates the responses obtained in pigeons (Kitchell *et al.*, 1959). In those animals in which we obtained a response to saccharin, if the saccharin was in distilled water,

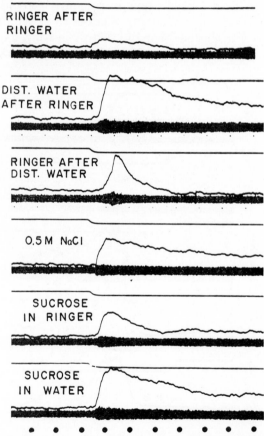

RINGER AFTER
RINGER

DIST. WATER
AFTER RINGER

RINGER AFTER
DIST. WATER

0.5 M NaCl

SUCROSE
IN RINGER

SUCROSE
IN WATER

Fig. 6.—Electrical responses from the whole chorda tympani of *Macacus rhesus* to the application of various solutions to the tongue. In each tracing are recorded, from top to bottom: the signal showing the moment of application, the integrated response, and the direct spike response. Time in seconds. (Reproduced from: Gordon, G., R. Kitchell, L. Strom, and Y. Zotterman. 1959. The response pattern of taste fibres in the chorda tympani of the monkey. Acta Physiol. Scand., **46**:119.)

we obtained a response of different character than when it was dissolved in Ringer's solution. (In 50 per cent of the pigeons studied, there was no response at all to saccharin in Ringer's solution, but there was always a response to saccharin in distilled water. The response to saccharin in distilled water was no different from that to distilled water alone.) It is also interesting to observe the response to a substance like ethylene glycol which, when placed upon the tongue of the pigeon, produced a slow-developing response which would reach its peak in about 90 seconds and then continue for more than 30 seconds, regardless of how much the tongue was rinsed.

I have discussed some of the features of the neural responses from a peripheral receptor field. I have pointed out variables which must be considered in obtaining, recording, and interpreting the neural responses.

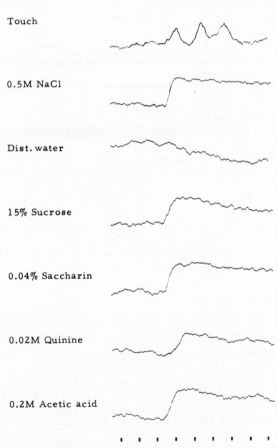

Touch

0.5M NaCl

Dist. water

15% Sucrose

0.04% Saccharin

0.02M Quinine

0.2M Acetic acid

Fig. 7.—Integrated responses of the whole chorda tympani nerve of *Homo sapiens* to various solutions flowed over the tongue. (Modified from: Zotterman, Y., and H. Diamant. 1959. Has water a specific taste? Nature, **183**:191.)

Ringer's sol.

0.06% Saccharin
in Ringer's sol.

0.06% Saccharin
in dist. water

15% Sucrose in
Ringer's sol.

15% Ethylene
glycol in
Ringer's sol.

0.2M Acetic
acid

TM 10 c.p.s.

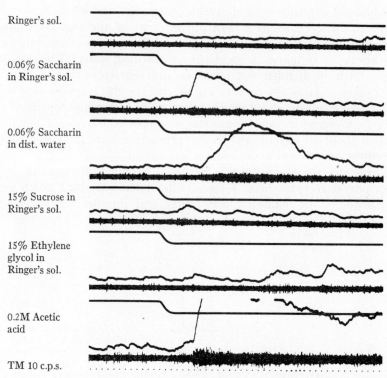

FIG. 8.—Records from lingual nerve of the pigeon. *In each record:* 1st, dispensing burette signal; 2d, integrated response; 3d, direct spike response. (Modified from: Kitchell, R. L., L. Strom, and Y. Zotterman. 1959. Electrophysiological studies of thermal and taste reception in chickens and pigeons. Acta Physiol. Scand., **46**:133.)

DISCUSSION

HALPERN: You spoke about measuring the fiber size in various nerves. Were you measuring axon-cylinder size or the whole myelineated sheath?

KITCHELL: Myelin-sheath size.

HALPERN: It has been shown that a considerable discontinuity between myelin-sheath size and axon cylinder may exist. There can be a relatively constant myelin sheath with a sizable difference in the axon within it (Sunderland and Roche, 1958). I wonder whether it might perhaps be appropriate to consider using a technique that can actually measure the axon cylinder itself.

KITCHELL: I certainly think that should be considered. We have done a large amount of fiber diameter sizing. I wanted to get my results consistent with that of other researchers, for comparative purposes, to see if the fiber diameter, including the myelin sheath, varied as the size of the animal varied.

JACOBS: Duncan (1960) recently reported behavioral rejection in the pigeon at all quinine hydrochloride concentrations from 0.1 per cent (0.0028M) to 2 per cent (0.055M). Can you get a rejection of something at low concentration and still not get electrophysiological recordings?

KITCHELL: I certainly think so. The evidence is that increasing the concentration will cross over the threshold for some of the receptors. If you go beyond physiological parameters, you may get responses. Also, a number of receptors will respond to different parameters beyond a certain range of stimulation.

JACOBS: Then the rejection of quinine could be on the basis of general chemoreception?

KITCHELL: Yes, and it could be on the basis of pain, that is, stimulation of pain receptors located on the tongue or elsewhere.

FISHMAN: Hodgson (1955), in a recent review paper, in listing some of the general aspects of chemoreception about which we need more information, said that what we need to learn more about is the mechanism by which impulses from the chemoreceptors initiate integrated response patterns of motor activity. Though his reference was to problems concerning invertebrate chemoreception, it is equally applicable to problems of vertebrate chemoreception. Purposeful response begins with information from the peripheral receptor, and the information from the receptor, of course, is coded and transmitted as the activities of peripheral afferent nerves.

Gustatory Afferent Responses in the Thalamus

Gabriel P. Frommer

In RECENT YEARS three lines of evidence have been presented to support Bornstein's contention that gustatory representation in the thalamus is closely allied with tongue tactile areas (Bornstein, 1940). First, thalamic lesions which result in taste deficits have been shown to involve the medial extension of the ventral basal complex in close association with the electrophysiologically defined tongue tactile region. Second, lesions in the cortical taste-projection area, and, in one case, in a peripheral nerve mediating gustation, have been found to result in degeneration of this thalamic structure. Third, electrophysiological activity ascribable to gustatory stimuli has been recorded from this thalamic site. We may also include here an experiment on the stimulation of the thalamus with chronically implanted electrodes. This resulted in behavior which, in the goat, was the typical "rejection response" to superthreshold acid or quinine solutions or very strong salt solutions. References to the pertinent literature may be found in Benjamin's recent contributions (Ables and Benjamin, 1960; Benjamin and Akert, 1959).

The purpose of this paper is to present in some detail the electrical activity as recorded from the thalamus in response to gustatory stimuli and to relate these findings to other experiments on the thalamic-gustatory relay. In addition to the work from the Brown laboratory (Pfaffmann *et al.*, 1961), to my knowledge only one electrophysiological experiment has been done on the gustatory-thalamic relay, and this was reported by Landgren (Appelberg and Landgren, 1958; Landgren, 1960*a*). During the course of some experiments on the thalamic tongue-projection area of *"encèphale isolé"* cats, a single unit was isolated which responded to 0.5M (3 per cent) sodium chloride and to no other stimulus, gustatory or otherwise.

The present experiments (Frommer, 1961) on thalamic gustatory activity have been performed on rats, usually females 200 to 300 grams in body weight, under nembutal anesthesia. Enameled nichrome wires 50 to 125 microns in diameter and exposed only on the cut end were used as recording electrodes. The standard stereotaxic apparatus with the ear bars was not used because of the possibility that the ear bars would interfere with conduction through the chorda tympani. The electrodes were oriented in the brain using empirical coordinates based on the coronal suture at the midline of the brain. The coronal and posterior sutures at the midline described a horizontal line, that is, the top of the rat's head was level. Typical ranges of coordinates for the responsive area were 3.8 to 4.2 millimeters posterior, 1.5 to 2.0 millimeters lateral, and 6.0 to 6.5 millimeters ventral. The activity was led through a Grass P-4 preamplifier, monitored with a cathode-ray oscilloscope and an audio monitoring system, and recorded permanently with an integrator system derived from Beidler's original circuitry. Occasional photographic records were made from a cathode-ray oscillograph placed in parallel with these systems.

It is usually possible to predict before one applies a physiological stimulus to the tongue whether the electrode lies within the primary relay nuclei of the thalamus. Characteristically, there is an irregular spontaneous background activity which, in the words of Mountcastle and Henneman (1949), "is audible over the loudspeaker as a continuous brushing of noise." This background is present only where strong responses to gustatory, tactile, or thermal stimuli are to be found. Weaker responses, reliably detectable only with the audio monitoring system, and with amplitudes usually less than about 50 microvolts with our conditions, are often observed independently of this background. These are presumed to be recorded from structures adjacent to the primary projection areas. When the electrode lies in the gustatory relay, application of the taste solution results in an asynchronous discharge maintained for the duration of the stimulus (Fig. 9) (Oakley, 1960). The response seems to be made up of a large number of units, none of which can be clearly isolated. Perhaps it is best described as a thickening of the base-line activity, although it is not as clearly differentiated from the background as responses recorded in the medulla (Pfaffmann *et al.*, 1961) (Fig. 10). In general, it seems to be similar in other respects to the response recorded at more peripheral sites.

When the thalamic response is put into the integrator, the resulting record is as illustrated in Figure 11. This figure reads from right to left and covers a total time of about $14\frac{1}{2}$ minutes. When recorded in this manner, the similarity of the results to those obtained at more peripheral loci is again strong. This record appears quite different from the integrator records that Kitchell showed because of a difference in time-constant and paper speed. In the response to 0.1M (0.55 per cent)

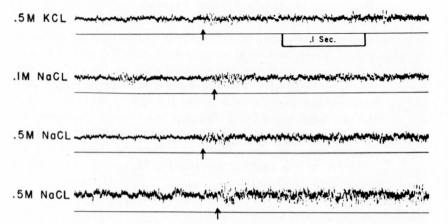

.5M KCL

.I Sec.

.IM NaCL

.5M NaCL

.5M NaCL

FIG. 9.—Rat thalamic gustatory response. From top to bottom: 0.5M KCl, 0.1M NaCl, 0.5M NaCl, and 0.5M NaCl. The bottom record is the response to 0.5M NaCl with the amplification twice that of the top three records. The approximate response onset is marked by an arrow. Note the typical spontaneous discharge in the beginning of the second record. Spike height varies from approximately 50 to 100 microv. 95 micron nickle-chrome electrode. Nembutal anesthesia. (Reproduced from: Oakley, B. 1960. Electrophysiologically monitored lesions in the gustatory thalamic relay of the rat. Sc.M. thesis, Brown University.)

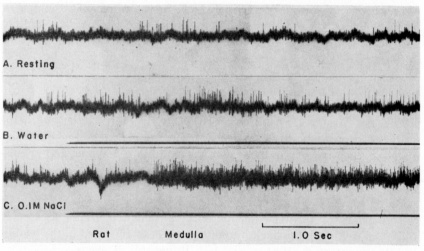

A. Resting

B. Water

C. 0.IM NaCl

Rat   Medulla   1.0 Sec

FIG. 10.—Oscillograph records showing electrical activity in the anterior tongue portion (solitary nucleus) of the bulbar gustatory relay following chemical stimulation of the tongue. The *uppermost trace (A)* shows resting activity, when no fluid flowed over the tongue. In the *second trace (B)*, water flow is indicated by the dark signal line. In the *bottom trace,* the signal line indicates the beginning of flow of 0.1 molar sodium chloride solution. A 50-micron electrode was used. (Modified from: Pfaffmann, C., R. P. Erickson, G. P. Frommer, and B. P. Halpern. 1961. Gustatory discharges in the rat medulla and thalamus, in: W. A. Rosenblith (ed.), *Sensory communication* [New York: John Wiley & Sons, Inc.].)

sodium chloride there is a very large initial swing; particularly note the response on the extreme left side of the figure, which goes off the record. This is followed by a decline to a lower level of activity which is maintained until the solution is washed off the tongue. The beginning of the steady-state may be seen in these records, and in other experiments we have obtained a relatively stable level of activity after the initial swing for as long as two minutes. The response to 1M (34 per cent) sucrose shows a slow rise time, and maximal activity, as recorded by the integrator, is present well after the stimulus flow has stopped (indicated by the stimulus marker at the bottom of the record).

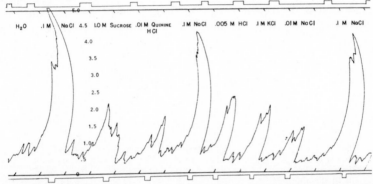

FIG. 11.—Fifteen-minute section of record (*read from right to left*) showing integrated thalamic-gustatory-relay responses to a series of taste stimuli recorded under optimal conditions (large response, small baseline variations). Rectangular deflections of bottom and top lines mark the duration of flow over the tongue of the taste stimulus and water rinse, respectively. Pips on the margin of the record are 1-minute intervals. Horizontal amplitude scale and curved vertical interval scale have been removed.

The integrated response to water is not greater than the "spontaneous" fluctuation of the base line.

In general, spontaneous activity is present in the vicinity of the thalamic nuclei mediating primary afferent activity, but it is not confined to these nuclei. It consists of a synchronized discharge of large amplitude, often greater than one hundred microvolts, which under our condition is quite large. In Figure 9 a burst can be seen in the left side of the second tracing. These "spontaneous" bursts are often much larger. They may come regularly spaced at about three to five bursts per second, or they may be at quite irregular intervals. Also, they often show a regular waxing and waning in time in the order of five to seven cycles per minute. Superimposed on this activity there may be a steady build-up of activity lasting for seven to ten minutes and terminating in an abrupt decline to the initial level. As one might suspect, this type of spontaneous activity plays utter havoc with the quantification of any but the strongest of the responses.

In eleven experiments in eighteen different loci, the response was large enough, as compared to the fluctuation of the base line, to permit some quantitative interpretation. At each locus, the median response to five "spectrum" stimuli has been converted into the percentage of the response to 0.1M (0.55 per cent) sodium chloride at that site to permit pooling of data from different sites. The five spectrum stimuli were 0.1M sodium chloride, 0.1M (0.74 per cent) potassium chloride, 0.01M (0.36 per cent) quinine hydrochloride, 0.005M (0.018 per cent) hydrochloric acid, and 1M (34 per cent) sucrose. The medians of the converted values, across loci, are given in Table 1.

There is considerable variability present in the data; therefore, some statistical treatment is appropriate. Non-parametric analysis of variance indicates that the over-all difference between responses to

TABLE 1

CHEMICAL STIMULUS	RELATIVE RESPONSE MAGNITUDE		
	Thalamus	Medulla	Chorda tympani
0.1M NaCl................	100	100	100
0.1M KCl................	39.8	27.0	36.5
0.005M HCl..............	52.0	35.5	53.5
0.01M Quinine HCl........	21.8	22.8	15.5
1.0M Sucrose............	33.8	30.0	44.0

Relative response magnitude to taste "spectrum" stimuli in a peripheral nerve and in thalamic and bulbar relays mediating gustatory afferent activity. Medulla and chorda tympani data from: Halpern, B. P. 1959. Gustatory responses in the medulla oblongata of the rat. Ph.D. thesis, Brown University.

the five stimuli is significant (p < .001). To identify the differences more readily, the stimuli were arranged in descending order of response magnitude and neighboring pairs were compared. All the differences were significant (p < .01), except for the one between potassium chloride and sucrose (p ≫ .05).

It is not unlikely that there is inhomogeneity present in these data; that is, reliable differences may exist in the quantitative pattern of the responses between loci. For instance, Halpern (1959) has demonstrated in the medulla a relative increase in the magnitude of the response to sucrose with an increase in the depth of the recording electrode. While the present data do not permit any such definitive differentiation of loci, we may be able to shed some light on the matter when the response magnitudes are ranked from one to five in ascending order within individual loci. Consistently, 0.1M (0.55 per cent) sodium chloride produced the largest response and had rank five at all sites. Quinine at 0.01M (0.36 per cent) is generally the smallest, receiving a rank of greater than two only once (2.5). Hydrochloric acid received a rank of three or four except for one experiment (two loci). The ranks of these three stimuli show relative stability between experiments and between loci. On the other hand, the ranks of 0.1M (0.74 per cent) potassium chloride and 1M (34 per cent) sucrose are spread relatively evenly over ranks one through four. This may indicate that some sort of differentiation of loci can be made in terms of the relative response magnitude of these two substances, but no anatomical correlation can yet be made.

Comparison of the spectra obtained from the peripheral nerve and

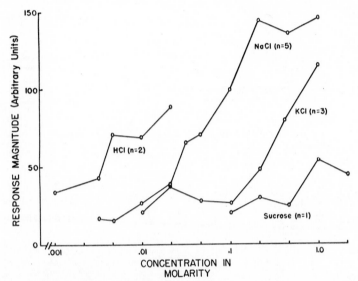

Fig. 12.—Thalamic-gustatory-relay median integrated neural response magnitudes following chemical stimulation of the tongue with various solutions. *Ordinate* represents magnitude of the integrated neural response in arbitrary units, adjusted to 100 units for the response to 0.1 molar sodium chloride solution. The "n" associated with the curves represents the number of experiments in each. Not every experiment is represented at each point.

the medulla with that presented here shows there is considerable similarity between the levels (Table 1). The ordering of 0.1M (0.55 per cent) sodium chloride > 0.005M (0.018 per cent) hydrochloric acid > 1M (34 per cent) sucrose ≥ 0.1M (0.74 per cent) potassium chloride > 0.01M (0.36 per cent) quinine seems to hold for all of them.

Some intensity-series data are available from the thalamus (Fig. 12). In the plot of the response magnitude against the log stimulus concentration, the sodium chloride series seems to show a positive acceleration over most of the values obtained. It shows an abrupt break at about 0.2M (1.1 per cent) sodium chloride and then flattens out. This break seems to appear fairly consistently in all of the experiments on which there are relevant data. Potassium chloride has a suggestion of a break

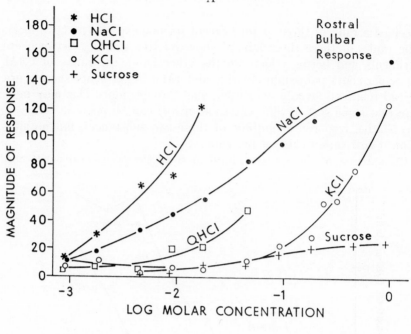

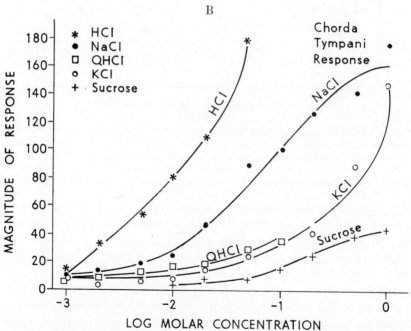

FIG. 13.—Median integrated neural response magnitudes following chemical stimulation of the rat's anterior tongue. *Ordinate* as in Fig. 12. (*A*) Rostral bulbar gustatory relay (solitary nucleus) responses; (*B*) Chorda tympani nerve responses. (Modified from: Halpern, B. P. 1959. Gustatory responses in the medulla oblongata of the rat. Ph.D. thesis, Brown University.)

at 0.1M (0.74 per cent). If this is compared with intensity series obtained in the periphery and the medulla (Halpern, 1959) (Fig. 13), there is no great difference in form.

Figure 14 shows the best histological verification so far obtained from any experiments yielding quantifiable response. In this preparation, responses to gustatory stimuli were obtained in the last 0.3 millimeter of ventral penetration of the electrode, which was stopped when the response began to drop out. This is the farthest penetration we were able

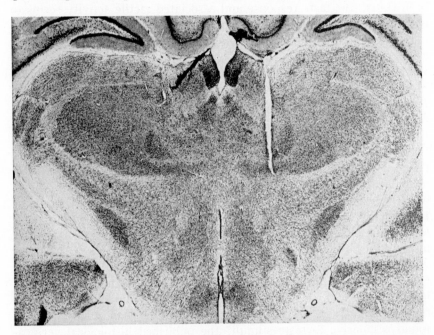

Fig. 14.—Thionine-stained section through a rat's diencephalon, showing an electrode track passing through the medial extension of the ventral nucleus of the thalamus and terminating at the ventral edge. Strong responses to gustatory stimuli were recorded in the last 0.3 mm. of the track. Further penetration was stopped when the response began to drop out.

to find in the histology. The tonguelike medial extension of the nucleus ventralis (De Groot's [1959] terminology for tactile relay nucleus in the rat) approximately encompasses the last 0.3 millimeter of the track (corrected for approximately 15 per cent expansion of the brain from the fixation and the sectioning technique), which leads to the conclusion that this structure is the thalamic relay mediating taste. Other histological materials seem to verify this conclusion. Strong taste responses are confined to the tonguelike extension located under the nucleus parafascicularis; sites only slightly lateral to it show only tongue temperature and tactile responses. Loci anterior to the main portion of this extension or on its posterior border seem to show only relatively weak responses to taste stimuli. Some little overlap has been observed between taste, temperature, and tactile modalities. Of these, taste seems to be the most independent.

While tactile responses often can be detected at the taste loci, mainly using the audio monitor, much stronger representation is found independently and overlapping temperature. Taste and temperature are seldom significantly overlapping in the thalamus of the rat. When it has been tested, the taste response and associated tactile activity seems to be ipsilateral, but since the rat tongue is rather small, it is often difficult to be certain. Temperature and other tongue tactile responses, however, are contralateral in origin.

There is much less ipsilateral tactile representation than described by Mountcastle and co-workers (Mountcastle and Henneman, 1949, 1952; Rose and Mountcastle, 1952) in cat, rabbit, and monkey. In their correlation of the physiologically defined thalamic tactile area with their ventrobasal complex, Rose and Mountcastle (1952) have proposed that the medial extension of the nucleus arcuatus, which is part of the ventrobasal complex in the cat and monkey, be included with the ventromedial rather than the ventrobasal complex of the thalamus. They based this assignment on cyto-architectonic evidence as well as on the functional ground that this extension is not activated by tactile stimuli to the body surfaces. They propose further that this structure may mediate gustatory or interoceptive activity.

Landgren's experiments (Appelberg and Landgren, 1958; Landgren, 1960*a*, *b*) on the tongue thalamic-projection area in the cat seem to be in agreement with this type of interpretation. While extensive tongue tactile and temperature phenomena were observed, only one unit was found responsive to taste stimuli; the published histological verifications presented suggest that Landgren was working mainly in the nucleus arcuatus as defined by Rose and Mountcastle (1952) and not in the medial tonguelike extension. To the extent that these structures are described herein for the rat, and are homologous to those on the cat and other species, the present findings would seem to fit fairly well with these results. However, one might question the usefulness and validity of assigning our tonguelike medial projection to the ventromedial complex, at least in the rat. The extension appears in our histological material to be quite homogeneous with the rest of the ventrobasal complex or the ventral nucleus of De Groot and independent of the ventromedial nucleus. This differentiation is in agreement with what De Groot (1959) shows in his atlas.

Benjamin and Akert (1959) have identified the medial extension as part of the subnucleus of the ventral nucleus extending laterally into a region where we and also Benjamin (see below) have been able to re-

cord only tactile responses. In addition, there is some functional similarity between the taste relay and the neighboring tactile relays. Besides
the fact that they mediate primary afferent activity, which seems to
follow a parallel course at least from the medulla to the cortex, there is
also the similarity in the spontaneous activity of the two regions.

Two experiments have recently demonstrated taste deficits following
thalamic lesions in the rats. I will describe the one done by Oakley
(1960, 1961) in which he placed lesions at sites from which he could
record electrical activity by electrophysiological methods. The purpose
of this procedure was to permit placement of very circumscribed
lesions to obtain taste deficits, with subsequent histological analysis.
Unfortunately, the electrophysiological localization was of very little
help in placing the lesions. It was necessary to place rather large
lesions, larger than the electrophysiologically delimited area, to get a
good taste deficit. Oakley was able to demonstrate an elevated preference threshold using sucrose and salt solution as well as the more usual
quinine-aversion test. In the sucrose and the sodium chloride tests,
there was abolition of any preference for these two stimuli. From the
preliminary histological verification available, it would seem that the
effective lesion would involve most or all of the subnucleus described by
Benjamin and Akert (1959).

In summary, the responses to gustatory stimuli may be recorded
from the medial extension of the ventral nucleus of the thalamus. The
ventral nucleus of the thalamus is the homologue of Rose and Mountcastle's ventrobasal complex (Rose and Mountcastle, 1952). These responses have properties similar to those observed in many peripheral
sites, and the localization of the responsive area is in good agreement
with tongue experiments on thalamic lesions resulting in taste deficits.

BENJAMIN

Our results from both lesion and recording studies fit quite precisely
with those which Frommer has just described. Previously, we had
found that thalamic retrograde degeneration from ablations of the
cortical taste area was confined to this region of the rat thalamus,
which, with only a little imagination, could be distinguished in normal
material as a morphologically distinct nucleus (Benjamin and Akert,
1959). Its extent is indicated by the solid block in the top row of cross
sections in Figure 15. These are serial sections taken at intervals of
approximately 0.3 mm., the most anterior to the left. The other three
rows are sample reconstructions from some forty cases of thalamic
lesions (Ables and Benjamin, 1960). A lesion which destroyed the
medial two-thirds of this nucleus throughout its length (case five) completely eliminated saccharin preference and raised quinine thresholds
some 20 times. This was a permanent deficit. A larger lesion including

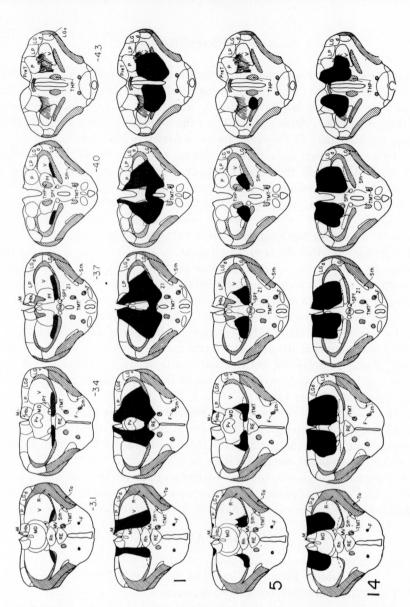

FIG. 15.—Cross sections of rat's thalamus at five successive levels. Most anterior section at the left. Serial frozen sections, 0.3 mm. apart, thionine stain. *Top row:* Retrograde degeneration due to ablation of cortical taste area. *Other rows:* Reconstructions of direct thalamic lesions. (1) Large lesion including medial portion of nucleus ventralis. Deficits produced not greater than in (5): Lesion restricted to medial two-thirds of nucleus ventralis. Permanently eliminated saccharin preference and raised quinine threshold by a factor of 20. (14) Large lesions which spared medial two-thirds of nucleus ventralis. No taste deficits noted. F = fornix, Hbl = lateral habenular nc., LGd = dorsal lateral geniculate body, LGv = ventral lateral geniculate body, LP = nc. lateralis posterior, M = medial habenular nc., MD = nc. medialis dorsalis, MV = nc. medialis ventralis, P = nc. posterior, Pf = nc. parafascicularis, $Pre\ T$ = pretectal nc., Pv = nc. paraventricularis, R = nc. reticularis, $Re\ (RE)$ = nc. reuniens, SPf = nc. subparafascicularis, Sth = nc. subthalamicus, THP = habenulointerpeduncular tracts, TMT = mammillothalamic tract, To = optic tract, V = nc. ventralis, ZI = zona incerta. (Modified from: Ables, M. F., and R. M. Benjamin. 1960. Thalamic relay nucleus for taste in albino rat. J. Neurophysiol., **23**:376.)

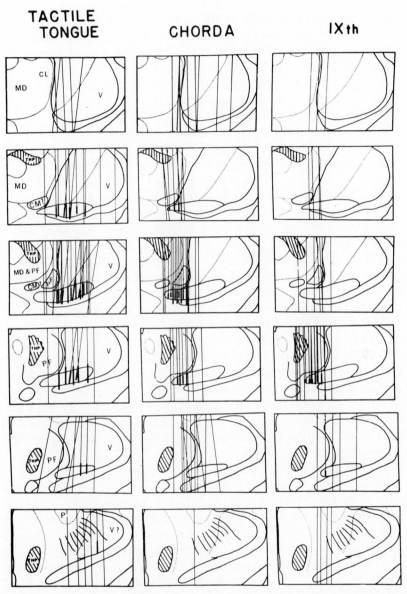

TACTILE TONGUE   CHORDA   IXth

FIG. 16.—Results of recording neural responses in the thalamus to tactile stimulation of the rat's tongue, or electrical stimulation of the chorda tympani nerve or glossopharyngeal (IXth) nerve. The areas responsive to each type of stimulation are indicated by the *dark bars* on the light lines which represent the course of the exploring electrode. The nucleus ventralis is seen on the middle four sections. Anterior is up. Abbreviations as in Fig. 15.

much of the surrounding tissue did not result in a more severe deficit (case one) and, conversely, destruction of this surround, sparing the nucleus, left an animal normal (case 14). The medial part of the nucleus was crucial. To get a clear-cut behavioral impairment, it was necessary to clean out thoroughly from front to back the medial part of the nucleus. Leaving a small amount intact at either end produced an animal with only a transient deficit or none at all.

On the basis of these results, it appeared that the medial part of this nucleus was the thalamic relay for taste. Recording studies pointed to the same conclusions (Emmers *et al.,* 1960). In Figure 16 responses are indicated by solid bars on the reconstructed electrode tracks. The nucleus is outlined on the middle four cross sections. Anterior is at the top. Tactile stimulation of the tongue evoked responses only in the lateral part of this nucleus. Electrical stimulation of the taste nerves, however, evoked activity in the medial part of the nucleus, the chorda tympani anterior to the IXth nerve. This would indicate, as Frommer has demonstrated so well, that the medial part of this nucleus is taste and probably purely taste and the lateral part is tactile and probably purely tactile, with an area of overlap between the two.

Appelberg and Landgren (1958) suggest that in the cat there may be overlap of taste and touch in the thalamus as well as the cortex (Cohen *et al.,* 1957; Landgren, 1957). We believe that this is incorrect. In the published photomicrograph (Appelberg and Landgren, 1958) they note that tactile responses are obtained laterally, the medial part of the nucleus being empty. Since they used gustatory stimuli only when they isolated a single unit, it may be that this part of the nucleus was not explored for chorda tympani responses, which, on the basis of the rat data, is where they should be found.

The same separation of taste and touch appears at the cortical level as well, at least in the monkey (Benjamin and Emmers, 1960). That is, electrical stimulation of either taste nerve produces two responsive areas, one within the tactile tongue area and one situated outside the tactile cortex. We assume the latter to be taste, though this must be verified directly with microelectrode recording. Electrical stimulation of the chorda and tactile stimulation of the tongue have been reported to activate the same cortical area in the cat (Cohen *et al.,* 1957; Landgren, 1957). If the cat is like the monkey, there should be a second chorda area, possibly in the presylvian fissure, which would be the true taste cortex.

DISCUSSION

KITCHELL: Can you say that you have not stimulated any tactile fibers in the chorda?

BENJAMIN: We cannot. We conclude that taste lies in the medial part of the nucleus by a process of subtraction. If we stimulate the whole tongue tactilely, we never get tactile responses medially. Therefore, if we get responses medially when we stimulate the chorda tympani, which contains both taste and tactile fibers, then these must be due to fibers other than tactile.

KITCHELL: I would like to correct a statement which I think is erroneous, which is that Landgren did not explore that area. He explored it many times; I was right there with him when he did so.

BENJAMIN: In describing the photomicrograph (Appelberg and Landgren, 1958), he states that he never gets tactile responses medially. As far as I could determine, he never mentioned chorda tympani responses in this medial location. Of course, I have only the publication as my source.

KITCHELL: No, but he went down through that area, and each time that he went through he explored it with touch and he explored it with taste solutions. He went right through that area all the time.

BENJAMIN: In later papers Landgren (1960*a, b*) reported that he used a negative focal potential with a 3–4 msec. latency, which he evoked with electrical stimulation of the ipsilateral tip of the tongue or of the lingual nerve, as a guide in locating the tip of the microelectrode within the nucleus. He pointed out (Landgren, 1960*b*) that this procedure might be likely to locate only the tactile pathway and might give no information on the gustatory pathway. In the rat he would not find any taste responses in this location. I think Frommer could confirm this.

FROMMER: I have never tried electrical stimulation of the tongue, but, from the characteristics of the physiological response, I am quite sure that the maximal response to electrical stimulation of the tongue would be more lateral than in the medial tip of the subnucleus.

KITCHELL: What size electrodes were you using?

BENJAMIN: They were stainless steel electrodes, 15 to 60 microns at the tip.

KITCHELL: Landgren used one to five micron electrodes (Appelberg and Landgren, 1958). It may be that when he was attempting to record from there he was not able to get responses from small cells in the vicinity, whereas you could with your large electrode.

BENJAMIN: That is quite possible.

HALPERN: Landgren might well have missed a taste-response area using tactile stimulation as a searching method. This would be the case in the solitary nucleus in which, with a multi-unit preparation, I could find chemically responsive areas which had no tactile responses at all. Other areas had both tactile and gustatory input. If I had searched only with tactile stimulation first and used this as a determination of the place to try chemicals, the purely chemoreceptive populations would have been missed (Halpern, 1959).

KITCHELL: That is quite understandable. The route for projection is generally thought to be through the spinal root of the trigeminal for tactile responses, whereas the gustatory route is thought to be in the solitary nucleus and fasciculus. They would converge in the thalamus.

HALPERN: In some single units in the solitary nucleus, one can record responses following tactile, thermal, and taste stimulation of the tongue (Pfaffmann *et al.*, 1961). With 25 micron electrodes in the solitary nucleus, I could sometimes get temperature, tactile, and taste responses from a group of units, all of them presumably in the solitary nucleus (Halpern, 1959). Fishman (1957) has published data indicating that in the same single chorda tympani fiber he can record responses to chemicals and to thermal stimulation of the tongue, so it need not be thalamic, or cortical, or even bulbar convergence.

KITCHELL: You are saying two different things. You said the tactile receptive areas were separate, and now you say they are together.

HALPERN: Sometimes one can record from a bulbar population which is only chemoreceptive. Sometimes one can record from another bulbar neuron population which receives chemical, thermal, and tactile input. There may be ordering there. There are experiments under way now at Brown looking for such ordering. The present data do seem to indicate that at least some of the single units (at the level of the primary neuron, the medulla oblongata, the thalamus, and the cerebral cortex) are responsive to more than chemicals. They are responsive to chemicals, to thermal, and also to mechanical stimulation. The fibers that are described as mechanoreceptors responsive to cold are analogous. I could call these "taste" units mechanoreceptors responsive to taste or temperature receptors responsive to chemical and tactile stimulation.

FROMMER: The question I would raise here is the relative magnitude of this overlap versus the independence. Our thalamic evidence suggests that the overlap with tactile input in the tongue taste region is relatively small, as compared to some of the independent responses that have been observed, but again this is unquantified. Responses from loci going to tongue tactile stimulation alone have been as large as 100 microvolts, while tactile responses evoked from taste loci are typically so small that they cannot be seen on the cathode-ray oscilloscope.

KITCHELL: What is the diameter of the medial area of the subnucleus of the thalamic nucleus ventralis?

BENJAMIN: It is about 250 microns vertically and less than 3/4 of a millimeter wide. It could be missed very easily.

KITCHELL: Three-quarters of a millimeter, and you are using a 20 micron diameter electrode. How many of those cells do you destroy as you go in?

BENJAMIN: A great many. I think the problem is missing the very small medial extension of the nucleus.

FROMMER: I can vouch for its being very easy to miss. I have been working on this for more than two years now. Part of the trouble has been with spontaneous activity. The other part of the trouble is unsuccessful preparations by simply missing the area, puncture after puncture.

TEPPERMAN: I would like to ask Frommer and Benjamin whether they have ever seen any obese animals that have had bilateral thalamic lesions.

BENJAMIN: None of our animals with thalamic lesions have become obese; on the contrary, they are quite lean. They have problems in eating, especially with large lesions which extend out into the tactile area.

FROMMER: Oakley (1960) has found that his taste-deficit animals are smaller than unoperated animals of the same age.

TEPPERMAN: In 1942 or 1943, Ruch and Patton were exploring in the thalamus, making lesions in the monkey. They had one monkey that I remember particularly—he weighed something like $16\frac{1}{2}$ or 17 kilos. He had all the diseases in the insurance actuary's files (cited in Soulairac, 1947).

CHAPTER 4

Interactions of Suprathreshold
Taste Stimuli*

Francis J. Pilgrim

Perhaps this session would better be termed "molar taste behavior," since both of the papers will be concerned with the response of the whole organism. My report is concerned with the intensive dimension, and it is on the interactions of suprathreshold taste stimuli. Dr. Joseph M. Kamen of our laboratory is responsible for the planning and interpretation of these experiments (Kamen *et al.*, 1961).

There have been no systematic investigations of taste interactions at suprathreshold stimulus intensities across all four taste qualities reported in the literature. Anderson (1950) had presented a review of the literature and the results of his own study at near-threshold concentrations. Even earlier, Fabian and Blum (1943) had summarized the literature on taste interactions and their own investigations on interactions between sweet, salty, and sour substances. However, their emphasis was on the effect of a subthreshold concentration of one substance on a suprathreshold concentration of another. Recently, Beebe-Center *et al.* (1959) have reported on interactions of suprathreshold concentrations of salt and sucrose. Their major conclusion was that some enhancement of sweetness by salt was evident in the case of weak solutions, but that the principal effect was the one of masking.

We are assuming the existence of four basic taste qualities: salt, sweet, sour, and bitter, and have assumed also that an appropriate stimulus for each is, respectively: sodium chloride, sucrose, citric acid, and caffeine. The interactions investigated were those between every pair of qualities, and in each given pair a stimulus was studied both as to its effect on another and how it was affected by the other. The taste solutions are in two series—a primary, or "effect on," and a secondary, or "effect of." The concentrations in the primary series were intended

* Based on material first presented at the 67th Annual Convention, Amer. Psych. Assn. Kamen, J. M., and F. J. Pilgrim. 1959. Interaction of taste qualities. Amer. Psychologist, **14**:429.

to cover the range of intensities from barely perceptible to almost extreme. On the other hand, the concentrations in the secondary series were intended to result in perceived intensities from none to a moderate level of intensity. It was thought that the interaction effects would be most easily demonstrated with such a series in which the secondary stimuli were generally of lower intensity than the primary ones. The actual selection of the levels used was based upon other data in our laboratory. I will not give the levels in terms of the concentrations but rather in terms of subjective intensity; thus the qualities or stimuli are all in similar ranges. The primary stimuli run from slight to very strong intensity; the secondaries from none to a moderate intensity. For each experiment, there were four levels of the primary stimulus and four levels of the secondary or background stimulus. This gives a four by four design, a total of 16 complex stimuli for each of the 12 possible pairs of the four qualities. The integrator was the central nervous system, and the recording instrument was a ball-point pen.

Responses were recorded in the laboratory on a rating scale for intensity (Fig. 1), which we found from past studies (Schutz and Pilgrim, 1957) to be quite effective in eliciting responses to stimuli varying in intensity. There are eight such scales on a sheet. The numbers at the bottom are just to guide the tabulators. They are the numbers that are actually used for the statistical analyses. I might point out that in this earlier work we found that mean ratings on this scale are fairly linear against log concentration of stimuli. A separate analysis of variance was performed for each taste-interaction experiment, and the sources of variation and their corresponding degrees of freedom, mean squares, and levels of significance have all been placed in a single table which is available in the complete report (Kamen *et al.*, 1960). With a four by four design, we did not choose to ask subjects to rate all 16 stimuli. The subjects are from our pool of 700 that are used mainly for food preference tests. They do not usually participate in the more elaborate psychophysical-type studies, so it is necessary for morale or motivation purposes to limit the number of treatments or stimuli given. The design used is technically termed a half-replicate, which splits the samples into two groups so that certain effects are confounded with the judge-group effect. Each of the mean ratings was based upon 40 judgments, that is, 40 subjects judged each of the eight stimuli, and another group of 40 subjects judged the other eight. The subjects were replaced in this pool and could be withdrawn again on a random basis for the subsequent 11 experiments. The 12 experiments were stretched out over a year so that some people did participate by chance more than once.

I have attempted to summarize the results for each of the pairs on the graphs. The graphs do not have the lines fitted to the points; rather, they are an indication of whether a particular effect in the analysis of variance was significant or not. Since there are four levels, one can analyze out a linear or general trend effect and a quadratic or curvi-linear effect. One can also analyze the cubic or double-inflection effect, but we felt that this would be a peculiar response, confounded with judge group. If we get a cubic effect, we do not know whether it is just the difference in level of the two groups or is real. Therefore, the discussion will be limited to the linear and the quadratic curvilinear effects.

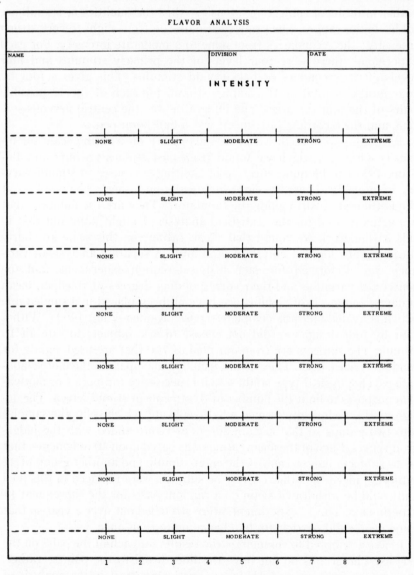

FIG. 1.—Intensity rating scale. The numbers at the bottom are to guide the tabulators

The first series across the top is the effect of caffeine upon the perception of the other qualities (Fig. 2). Of course, before the experiment the subjects were oriented; they were told, for example, in the first one: "Rate the saltiness of each of the solutions and ignore any other flavors that are present." For each of the four salt levels, they had some with

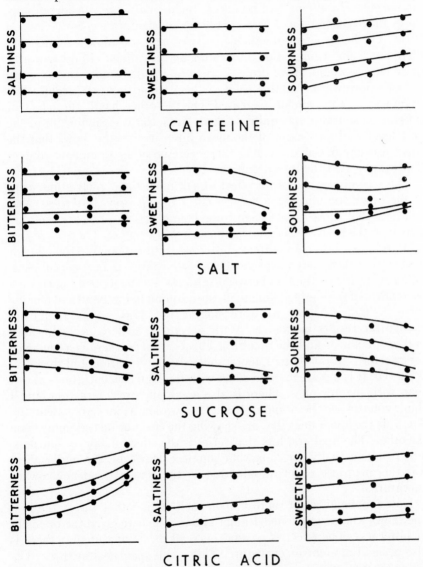

Fig 2.—Summary of taste interactions. The abscissa represents increasing concentrations of the secondary stimulus. The four curves in each graph are for the four levels of the primary stimulus whose taste quality is shown on the ordinate. (Reproduced from: Kamen, J. M., F. J. Pilgrim, N. J. Gutman, and B. J. Kroll. 1960. Interactions of suprathreshold taste stimuli. QMFCIAF Report No. 14–60, Project 7-85-15-007.)

no caffeine, with a very slight amount of caffeine, and then on up to a moderate intensity of bitterness due to the caffeine. As is evident from the first graph in Figure 2, there were no significant effects of caffeine upon saltiness. This was true regardless of the level of caffeine. Saltiness was merely a function of the salt concentration itself. The same is true for sweetness; caffeine had no effect. Incidentally, we considered only those that reached the 1 per cent level of significance as having an effect. The linear effect of caffeine on sweetness was almost significant; there was a slight suggestion of masking by the caffeine. In other words, those curves would, if we drew them to fit the data more closely, tend to slope downward slightly: each of them would indicate slightly less sweetness as the caffeine increased. On the other hand, the effect of caffeine on sourness was quite marked. In fact, it was significant at the .001 level, and inspection of the mean intensity ratings shows that the effect was one of enhancement; there were no other significant sources that complicated the interpretation.

The second row shows the effect of salt upon the perceived intensity of the other stimuli. There was no effect of salt upon bitterness. You will note that those points seem to be bouncing a bit, but the lines are drawn on the basis of the non-significance of the effect. There were certain problems with this saltiness-bitterness interaction. We thought for a while that there may have even been some confusion in some subjects' minds as to the distinction between saltiness and bitterness. Therefore, we replicated the study, giving them pure stimuli beforehand and naming them, to indicate what we were looking for. This, however, did not change the results in this set. With sweetness we have a significance both of the linear and the quadratic effects; that is, there is a tendency for sweetness to fall off with increasing salt concentration, but the effect is curved. It is a more marked effect with the high concentrations of salt than with the low ones. There is also a salt-sucrose interaction, and I think you can see the origin of that. The two lower lines are essentially flat; it is the upper ones that are showing the effect of one stimulus upon the other. The final graph in that series is the effect of salt on sourness. The results actually are somewhat complex. However, the major effect was the quadratic effect of salt, that is, the general tendency toward curvature.

Now for the effect of sucrose upon each of the other three; the first one shows what every coffee drinker knows: sugar reduced the intensity of bitterness. The effect is general over all levels of caffeine; there is also a small amount of curvature. This result may be stated as: The linear component was significant at the 0.001 level, whereas the curve was significant just at the 0.01 level. In the next graph sucrose had no general enhancing or masking effects on saltiness. There is also an indication that the relationship might be somewhat complex in that the highest sucrose concentrations cause some reduction of saltiness but only at alternate levels. The experiment was replicated another time, and the results are real. We feel that in some of these cases it may be necessary to test points in between in order to detect some of the irregularities; in other cases, to extend the range because it appears that effects might be showing up beyond the range we tested. For the effect of sucrose on sourness, it is evident again that the sugar reduces the intensity of the sourness, and the sharpest drop in intensity occurs with the higher sucrose concentrations.

The last series is the effect of citric acid upon the perception of the other qualities. Now, as is evident from the graph as well as from the levels of significance that we obtained, citric acid very markedly enhanced bitterness, and you will note that it had a stronger effect and greater upward slope on the low levels of caffeine than it did on the higher levels. This led to a citric acid–caffeine interaction.

In general, saltiness was enhanced by citric acid. The significance was at the 0.001 level. The enhancement has not been shown to be dependent upon the level of salt. Actually, the absolute increase was not very marked, but in this particular set the error term was one of the lowest in all of the interaction experiments. That is one thing I should point out. The error term, which represents the disagreement among judges as to the relative standing of the different stimuli (the solution-judge interaction), does vary from one pair to another. This is apparently not just a random effect of picking different judges, because all of these experiments were actually broken down into subsessions or replications. We find that with certain stimuli everybody tends to agree as to their intensity, whereas in other sets there is much disagreement, making for a much larger error term. Hence, in the latter case, one may get bigger over-all changes, but they may not be significant. The effect of citric acid on saltiness, although it looks from the curves as though there were very little effect, was actually highly significant because of the low error. For the last one, the effect of sour upon sweetness, citric acid generally increased sweetness. This is in agreement with the results of Fabian and Blum (1943). However, they had used only near-threshold concentrations of citric acid.

What I have attempted to do is to present a general exploration of taste interactions. It was determined in each case whether a secondary stimulus quality had an enhancing or a depressing effect or in some cases both effects or no effect upon a primary stimulus. In most cases the results were clear-cut. Functional relationships between the primary and secondary stimuli were either monotonic or nonexistent. Where ambiguities or hints of a trend with different concentrations occurred, we have made recommendations for follow-up research, such as testing between points or extending the ranges of stimuli. No secondary stimulus has a uniformly enhancing or depressing effect upon the remaining three primary stimuli, nor was any primary stimulus enhanced or depressed uniformly by the other secondaries. Further, what happened at near-threshold-stimulus concentrations was not necessarily predictive of suprathreshold phenomena.

DISCUSSION

PANGBORN: Dr. Pilgrim, did you check beforehand to see whether or not the subjects could distinguish between bitterness and sourness? Many people confuse the two.

PILGRIM: Well, I pointed out that in some cases we felt the subjects were confusing them, and we did give them sample stimuli with names before they started the actual session. This was not checked again afterward by asking them which is which.

ENGEN: Would you care to comment further on theoretical implications of the four qualities and the four chemicals you selected? Are we to hold on to the four basic qualities or should we give them up?

PILGRIM: I think we have gone along with the crowd. We recognize that these are at least nodal points that seem to be understandable to most people, even admitting one point of confusion between bitter and sour under some circumstances. There may be others; I won't dispute this. Certainly I think that since they have been used for so long it was at least worth starting off with these four qualities for an exploration of how they interact. Actually, the results may help to lead to other studies that could clear up this point; but I am reasonably happy with using these four for the time being.

GOLDSTEIN: Did I understand Engen to say that there is something suspect about these four taste qualities? This question has been bothering me. What is the status of these four now?

HALPERN: I suppose the answer depends on how one asks the question and of whom. The single-unit electrophysiological data seem to indicate that there isn't a neat physiological ordering of chemoreceptor units into salt, sour, sweet, and bitter categories. Rather, at their most specific, there will usually be some sort of combination of these categories which crosses over "quality" boundaries. At their least specific, single peripheral gustatory units will respond to almost anything you care to place on the tongue. Thus, in answer to a strictly electrophysiological question, one might say that these four categories are not reasonable. This says nothing about whether as a behavioral ordering by a human these are not reasonable categories. This is quite another question.

GOLDSTEIN: When one reads the human literature, it is in taste where the confusion about the number of qualities has been longest and most profound. I for one would accept the notion of patterning. It reconciles the animal data where there is no specificity, and the human information where there has been, until quite recently (within the last 50 years), no general agreement. This agreement on the four qualities is an agreement almost by default. People have stopped arguing about the question by not investigating it. I would raise the question, why in animal taste studies is the magic number still four? Why, when we could sample all of the stimuli that a chemist gives us, do we still restrict ourselves to four substances plus, on occasion, one or two more?

HALPERN: I do not think the magic number is necessarily still four. In the electrophysiological studies by Beidler (Beidler, 1953; Beidler *et al.*, 1955), and by Fishman (1957), a tremendous range of different chemicals is used. The behavioral experiments that are going on under the direction of Kare on animal taste preference are using almost every available chemical that does not immediately kill the animal (e.g., Ficken and Kare, 1961).

GOLDSTEIN: It seems to me that we are at the point of considerable clarification. Here we have a single-fiber analysis. We know that there is a pattern. We could go ahead and ask a very profound and basic question: What are the characteristics of these fibers? I am a little surprised to find out that with the possibility of a clarification right at hand a good number of people are primarily interested in four taste substances.

MORRISON: Of course, I agree with Halpern, but I would like to ask, what would I tell an introductory psychology class?

HALPERN: I would tell a class in introductory psychology that there are certain chemical compounds which, when used as taste stimuli, are followed by, in the majority of human beings, characteristic verbal responses. When used with animals, these chemicals support characteristic avoidance behaviors or approach behaviors, sometimes with no need to adduce learning. If, however, one then tries to take these behavioral categories and relate them to chemical orderings of compounds, one very quickly runs into trouble. No simple or complex chemical ordering of compounds seems to relate consistently to human experiences or to avoidance or selection behavior in animals. Kare pointed this out in discussing possible chemical ordering to relate to the preference behavior for the sugars that he has studied (Kare and Medway, 1959). Other investigators have made such attempts (Ferguson and Lawrence, 1958; Lawrence and Ferguson, 1959). This is the difficulty: The chemical ordering and the physiological ordering do not seem to fit together at this point. Perhaps we do not know enough about the chemical ordering.

PANGBORN: We have published on taste experiments on human subjects who evaluated the same compounds Pilgrim has just listed (Pangborn,

1960). Our judges were trained for a period of six weeks before the experimental conditions were initiated. It has been our experience that a minimum of three weeks is required before the individual ceases to alter his response as a result of training. A multiple-comparison methodology patterned after that described by Fabian and Blum was used. This may account, in part, for differences in findings between our work and that described by Pilgrim. Using reagent grades of sucrose, sodium chloride, caffeine, and citric acid, we found that, without exception, subthreshold, threshold, and suprathreshold levels of the four compounds depressed the taste intensities of each other. The most pronounced depression was the sucrose–citric acid effect, i.e., all levels of sucrose caused citric acid to appear less sour; all levels of citric acid caused sucrose to appear less sweet. These results were verified using fruit nectar as the taste solution. In nectars, flavor is an additional contributing factor, yet the four compounds still depressed the intensity of each other.

JACOBS: I gather that you were implying that the major differences in results could be explained by the fact that you had more sophisticated subjects. In terms of the discussion up to this point, I wonder whether either set of these results can be more easily explained by those of you who are working on taste from a physiochemical point of view. For example, if all the mixture interactions resulted in a reduction in intensity, would this be a simpler case to explain?

HALPERN: A paper from Zotterman's laboratory has reported on responses to citric acid–sucrose mixtures recorded from single fibers in the dog (Andersson, 1950). First the response frequency for sucrose alone, and then for citric acid alone, was determined; the two were then given as a mixture. It was reported that algebraic summation of the responses to the two individual chemicals alone was obtained. That is, if 20 pulses per second were recorded for one and 40 for the other, putting them together as a mixture gave 60 pulses per second. It was concluded that non-algebraic-summation interactions of citric acid and sucrose, which they felt were "common experience," must be occurring at some point further up in the nervous system. More recently, this phenomenon has been studied with acetic acid and sucrose, using the intact chorda tympani nerve of the rat and an integrator (Halpern, 1959). The mixture results were close to algebraic summation. (There was a trick involved: the two compounds, individually, had to produce about the same response magnitude. If one mixed a concentration of acid that gave a large response and a concentration of sucrose that gave a small response, the effects of the addition were difficult to see. Perhaps all the sensory channels were being used by the stronger stimulus.) If one had sucrose and acetic acid solutions which gave the same response individually, and then used an equivalent mixture, the peripherally recorded response magnitude came very close to doubling. However, using the same mixtures and recording from the solitary nucleus in the medulla oblongata (past the first synapse in the taste system), the response magnitude less closely approached an algebraic summation (Halpern, 1959).

There are difficulties with this sort of analysis because it is an integrator study and, therefore, as pointed out by Kitchell, there are possibilities of temporal overlap between firing units producing some of these differences. There were, however, some indications of a difference between responses in the first- and second-order neuron pools, the difference going toward the generally found behavioral data.

In behavioral terms, one might say that this means, looking at the central nervous effect and talking in terms of absolute magnitude of the response, that the sucrose–acetic acid mixture will be a stronger stimulus than one component alone but will not be as strong as the magnitude assigned to one component solution plus the magnitude assigned to the other. The central nervous system response is closer to the behavior data reported here than what occurred in the peripheral nerve.

PILGRIM: I think one large difference between the experiments Halpern is talking about and the type that both Pangborn and I are talking about is that you did not ask the nerve preparation the intensity of the stimulus for "sweet" or "sour." You took the total, whereas we asked how sweet the stimulus is or how sour or how bitter and please ignore the other perceptions. At least in ours we said "ignore the others."

HALPERN: A single-unit analysis might begin to approximate the kind of studies that you and Pangborn did.

GOLDSTEIN: Halpern said that when one records in the medulla, one obtains a decrease in the summated potential, and this agrees with the behavioral evidence. What sort of behavioral evidence?

HALPERN: Human responses. As Pilgrim pointed out, the verbal judgments obtained by both Pangborn (1960) and by him are restricted to one of the "taste qualities" elicited by the mixture. However, if a sucrose–organic acid mixture is reduced in both "sweetness" and "sourness," then the total magnitude of the response to the mixture must be less than the sum of the components.

GOLDSTEIN: I would like to caution against expecting to find exact correspondences between human verbal responses and the central nervous system code. I can imagine the opposite thing happening in the rat, and one could argue that sweetness with acetic acid, just as sweetness in lemonade, would actually reduce the sourness. It seems to me, though, that the real flaw in using your electrophysiological information as the real clue to behavioral studies is that one could theoretically argue strongly that the predisposing conditions that modify behavior are purely environmental. It is almost irrelevant, theoretically, what is going on in the central nervous system as long as it is reliably correlated with the behavioral changes.

HALPERN: I cannot really agree with your proposition. I think that peripheral electrophysiological data are a useful measure of the sensory information going into the animal. In the central nervous system the electrophysiological data indicate what happens to the sensory information. Does this not have rather significant relationships to behavior? Of course, one can work with the behavior and ignore the nervous system completely, but I think that there is more profit in considering both.

GOLDSTEIN: I would agree. My only point is that we must not allow ourselves to be too much bound up with this idea that our logic about behavior is the logic of the central nervous system. I am impressed by the fact that we have continually to change our ideas of the logic of the central nervous system as we know more and more about it, and all of the inferences that we make from behavior about the detailed firing and function of the central nervous system are always pale replicas of what we finally end up with when we explore the central nervous system correctly enough.

FISHMAN: I would like to add that chorda tympani experiments of my own on enhancement between salts bear out Halpern's results.

JACOBS: Phenomenological judgment by trained observers seems reasonably consistent concerning the four classical tastes. I know of no other adequate adjectives that are used to describe a taste quality by experimental subjects.

FROMMER: This sounds like an anthropological question, in the sense that we have been always trained to say: sweet, salty, bitter, and sour.

JACOBS: Well, I am not that familiar with the historical development of the subjective terms used to describe these things historically (see Boring, 1942, pp. 453–55, for the development of the taste "qualities").

MACLEOD: I think it's worth reinforcing the point that Goldstein made a little while ago that our number four is really the magic four. It has grown up; so far as I know, we have no real empirical descriptive studies of what is different from what for people in this culture and in other cultures at this age level, among children, and so forth. We have simply taken over these four primary things. I hope we can talk a little bit about the meaning of modality in sense perception.

KITCHELL: I think Kare would agree with me that we want to be extremely cautious in applying these to what an animal does.

KARE: I certainly would agree with Kitchell. However, I am afraid my comments will further complicate rather than simplify the problem. My considered judgment would be that the four qualities used to classify human taste response provide little or no basis for application in comparative work. We have used hundreds of compounds, including several dozen compounds in a homologous series, and observed no chemical continuity that might be correlated to the animal's taste reaction.

There are real differences in taste response to various materials between species, even a suggestion of breed or strain differences. Saccharin is a good example. It is commonly described as sweet to man and falls into a similar behavioral category for the rat. Using a concentration sweet to humans, it was observed to be unpleasant to the fowl and evoked an indifferent reaction in the majority of calves (Pick and Kare, 1959). Pigs, we found, fall into three categories insofar as their reaction to saccharin is concerned. Some find it pleasant, a second group is indifferent, and a sizable minority is offended by it in every concentration we tested (Kare *et al.*, in press). A similar if not parallel picture of absolute differences exists in our sugar studies with the various domestic animals.

We have tried to mask the offensiveness to the fowl of some water-administered medicinals. We added many compounds pleasant to humans but have never been able to reduce substantially the offensiveness. Perhaps this is related to the strong electrophysiological response to water evoked in the fowl (Halpern and Kare, 1961), which is not observed in humans (Zotterman and Diamant, 1959) or the rat (Zotterman, 1956).

The animal data we have not only challenge the concept of four taste qualities but question the application of any human judgments on taste to animals without prior testing.

ENGEN: I think this is a very interesting and exciting problem that we often overlook. We tend to forget that their four qualities probably came from man's experience, and we have to consider this whether we talk about animals or man. Finding the confusions which Pangborn and Pilgrim mentioned is a most interesting aspect of the four qualities. It is not clear to me what animal experiments could contribute to this problem.

PANGBORN: Perhaps we should speak in terms of the taste of a given compound rather than the "sweet" taste, the "sour" taste, the "bitter" taste, etc. When discussing results in electrophysiology, we should speak of the effect of sucrose rather than the sweet taste. My taste-panel members report that the sweetness of lactose differs from the sweetness of fructose or glucose even at the same relative sweetness intensity. Also, individuals with low fructose thresholds do not necessarily have low thresholds for glucose or lactose. The threshold for sucrose decreases with training, but, when the same judge is presented with fructose solutions, another training period is required. In other words, there is no carry-over of training from one sugar to another.

ENGEN: To come back to Kare's question, several classification systems have been suggested, but I have not seen one with much general support. I think you immediately run into the problem of learning. Before we can talk about any primary qualities, we must be able to distinguish what is learned from what is innate and that, of course, is a problem all by itself.

PILGRIM: We assumed that there were four primary qualities, and we assumed that these four substances were the best representatives of them.

ENGEN: I do not think any of us intended to blame you for the four qualities, but I am happy we discussed the problem.

Methodology in Preference Testing

Kent R. Christensen

AT FIRST I would like to confine my discussion to the methods which
P. T. Young has used throughout the years in the laboratories at Illinois. Following this I will give a more detailed account of the methods
which we are now using, since the incorporation of the electronic preference tester.

One of the early procedures which Young used was Richter's intake
method, in which an animal is presented with two bottles and intake is
measured over a period of time, generally 24 hours. A difficulty with
this method is that it fails to take account of the great complexity of
factors which determine intake. One of these factors is the functioning
of head receptors and the resulting palatability effect. Other factors are
the organic state of the animal, including states of depletion, need, and
satiation, the past history of the organism with respect to reinforcement
by foodstuffs, and constitutional factors (species differences).

In an attempt to obtain a more precise record of an animal's ingestive
behavior, Young next employed graphic methods, the first of which is
also an intake method (Young and Richey, 1952). This method utilizes
an inverted glass tube which contains a cork float suspending a non-
absorbent filament. (The filament, being non-absorbent, has the same
length in air as in water and solutions.) The filament is attached to an
ink recording-pen. As the subject drinks from a standard one-inch cup,
the fluid level and cork fall, causing a corresponding drop in the position of the pen. With this apparatus, permanent records of the rate and
frequency of drinking are obtained.

This method was satisfactory for continuous recording of intake
over periods of time as long as ten days. It did not permit fine discriminations over short periods of time because it was necessary for the subject to consume an appreciable volume of fluid before the pen position
changed. This limitation led to the development of another method
(Young, 1957a), similar to the one just described but much more sensitive. In the new method a boot-shaped nozzle is substituted for the drinking cup. The tip of the nozzle, which has a small aperture, is inside the

cage. The non-absorbent filament is led to the recording equipment through a capillary tube which constitutes the heel of the boot and is outside the cage. As the animal drinks from the nozzle, small air bubbles rise in the tube, and the float drops a bit every time a bubble rises to the surface. Sensitivity is further increased by the use of a narrower tube.

Young's earliest form of preference tester utilized exceedingly brief exposures (often less than one second) and forced an animal to make a

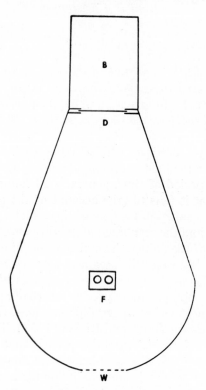

Fig. 3.—Floor plan of the Young brief-exposure preference tester. (*B*) starting box, (*D*) door, (*W*) observation window, (*F*) food cups. (Modified from: Young, P. T. 1944. Running activity and dietary habit of the rat in relation to food preference. Jour. Comp. Psychol., **37**:327.)

choice (Young, 1944). With the brief-exposure technique the quality of choice, rather than the duration of contact or the quantity of substance ingested, is the criterion of preference. The floor plan of Young's brief-exposure preference tester is shown in Figure 3.

In testing preferences with this apparatus, the experimenter first places the animal in compartment "B," the starting box, and after a delay (30 or 60 seconds), the door "D" is elevated and the animal is free to approach the food cups, which are located at a standard distance

(38 cm.) from the threshold of the door. The behavior of the animal at the food cups is observed through a window "W." The animal is allowed to take one food or to touch one and turn to the other, after which both cups are instantly dropped out of reach of the subject. The food cups are not raised to the feeding plate until the animal has returned to the starting box, but before they are raised their relative positions are interchanged by means of a turntable device. Since the animals are reinforced by a nibble or sip only when they approach the foods from the starting box, they learn to shuttle back and forth between box and foods, making a series of round trips. Every time an animal approaches

Fig. 4.—An electronic preference tester for simultaneous testing of the preferences of six rats. Each unit contains two graduated burettes. In one burette is a standard solution; in the other, a compound taste solution paired with the standard. P. T. Young is shown placing a rat in the first unit of the electronic preference tester.

the food cups, he has an opportunity to show a preference. With experienced animals a series of 10–30 choices can usually be observed in a testing period of 12–20 minutes. The activity of an animal upon the preference tester, of course, varies with the incentive values of the test foods as well as with other conditions.

The brief-exposure preference tester works well, and a good many studies have been made with it. The method, however, is time consuming and a bit laborious.

Presently, we are testing preferences with an electronic apparatus. Figure 4 shows a battery of electronic preference testers which we are now using at the University of Illinois. There are six boxes, each box holding one animal. Each box is equipped with two drinking tubes which generally contain different substances—simple or compound taste solutions. There are leads from the fluid in each tube and from the hardware-cloth floor of the cage to an amplification stage. Every time an animal makes contact with the fluid in a tube, he completes a circuit through his tongue. The animal serves as a switch in this respect. The subthreshold signal is amplified and led to a relay which actuates a counter or a cumulative recorder. Presently, we are using a panel of 12 counters—6 pairs of counters corresponding to the 6 pairs of test fluids. Rats lick rather uniformly at the rate of 6–8 contacts per second, and each separate lick is registered on one of the counters. A pair of counters is read once every 60 seconds, and the readings are recorded on a data sheet. The record shows the cumulative number of tongue contacts, minute by minute, throughout the exposure period.

Two methods of using the electronic preference tester have been tried. In one method (Young, 1960) the same two test fluids are presented simultaneously in all 6 boxes, and squads of 6 rats are tested at the same time. The animals are placed in the boxes successively at 10-second intervals. A pair of counters is read every 10 seconds throughout the exposure period (which may be 3 or 15 minutes). At the close of the exposure period, the animals are removed from the boxes, in the original order, at 10-second intervals. The record for each animal shows the cumulative number of contacts, minute by minute, throughout the exposure period. A preference is defined by the relative frequency of tongue contacts during the exposure period; the fluid receiving the greater number of contacts is regarded as the preferred fluid of a pair. This method of testing 6 animals at a time greatly speeds up the process of preference testing. We can readily test 30 or more animals in a reasonable time.

We have given series of daily tests. In a typical series the standard fluid remains unchanged, and the comparison fluid is systematically varied day by day. Thus, on a given day, the standard might be a sucrose solution of 1 per cent (0.03M) and the comparison a compound solution containing 32 per cent (0.93M) sucrose plus 0.001 per cent (0.00003M) quinine hydrochloride. In a series of tests the concentration of quinine is gradually stepped up, test by test, until a concentration is reached that is rejected by the animals. Rejection thresholds have been determined with sucrose standards of 1 per cent (0.03M), 2 per cent (0.06M), 4 per cent (0.12M), 8 per cent (0.23M), 16 per cent (0.47M), and 32 per cent (0.93M). Points of hedonic equality which determine an isohedon have also been located.

An *isohedon* may be defined as the locus of points, within a given sensation area, which are equally acceptable to the subject. In the field of taste, a sensation area can be defined by two variables such as the concentration of quinine hydrochloride and the concentration of sucrose within a single compound solution. Isohedons have been mapped objectively for the rat in three sensation areas: bitter-sweet, salt-sweet, and sour-sweet.

In the second method of using the electronic preference tester (Christensen, 1960), rats are tested individually instead of by groups of six. All boxes contain the same standard fluid but different comparison fluids.

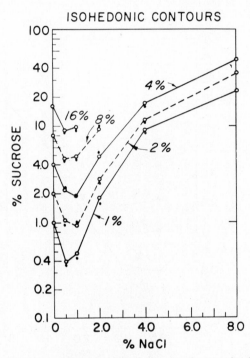

FIG. 5.—Sucrose–sodium chloride isohedon for the non-deprived rat

This method, which I have used in determining points on isohedons in the sucrose–sodium chloride area, is an adaptation of the so-called "up-and-down" or "staircase" method (Guilford, 1954). The method has made it possible to plot the isohedons which are shown in Figures 5 and 6.

The general question I asked can be illustrated by reference to the 1 per cent isohedon: How much sucrose must be added to a 1 per cent (0.17M) sodium chloride solution to make it equally acceptable to a simple 1 per cent (0.03M) sucrose solution with no added salt?

An answer was obtained as follows: Each of the six testing cages was fitted with one tube containing the standard sucrose solution (S) and another containing one of the comparison solutions (C). The left-right positions of standard and comparison tubes were uniform for all cages for a given day but alternated between days. During a specific test the comparison solutions all contained the same concentration of sodium chloride but different sucrose concentrations. Thus, for a given test, a standard solution was paired with a series of comparison solutions of equal salinity but differing in sucrose concentration. (The concentrations of sucrose used in the comparison solutions were determined by preliminary research.)

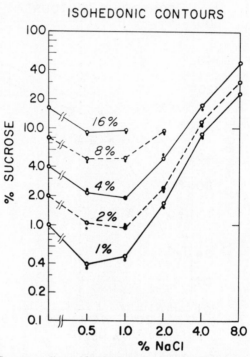

FIG. 6.—Sucrose–sodium chloride isohedon for the non-deprived rat

To illustrate more specifically: When locating the point on the 1 per cent sucrose isohedon which corresponds to 1 per cent sodium chloride, we placed in all six cages an S-tube containing 1 per cent sucrose and in each individual cage a C-tube containing 1 per cent sodium chloride plus one of the following concentrations of sucrose: 0.316 per cent (0.0092M), 0.40 per cent (0.012M), 0.50 per cent (0.015M), 0.63 per cent (0.018M), 0.80 per cent (0.023M), and 1.00 per cent (0.03M). The point of hedonic equality as determined by the "up-and-down" method was located at 0.47 per cent (0.014M), which is a point plotted on the graph.

In an actual test six rats are brought directly from their home cages to the laboratory. They are tested individually and promptly returned to their home cages. Then another six are brought to the laboratory. No animal is absent from its home cage for more than 30 minutes per test.

In giving tests, the rat was forced to sample both fluids separately before making a choice. First the S-tube was presented, and the animal was permitted 6–10 licks. Then the S-tube was withdrawn and the C-tube presented. Again, the animal was permitted 6–10 licks. The cycle was repeated so that every rat was forced to sample twice both test solutions. The two tubes were next presented together for choice, and a stop watch was started. No record was made during the first minute following the simultaneous introduction of both tubes. The total number of licks recorded during the next three minutes was our criterion of preference. The solution which under these conditions received the greater number of licks was assumed to be preferred. Shaping their drinking behavior took several weeks of pretraining.

In the "up-and-down" method the preference exhibited by one rat determines the test to be given to the next animal. Thus, if the first rat exhibited a preference for the comparison solution, the sucrose concentration of the comparison solution was, in effect, lowered one step for the next rat by placing it in the appropriate cage. If the first rat showed the opposite preference, the sucrose concentration of the comparison solution was, in effect, raised by placing the next rat in the appropriate cage. This procedure was followed for all succeeding animals. Each animal thus determined what comparison stimulus would be paired with the standard for the next animal, i.e., into which cage the next animal would be placed. With this method, all tests are automatically centered around the point of equal acceptability for the group of rats as a whole. The initial comparison solution is randomized over all tests.

When the proportion of animals preferring each of the comparison solutions is plotted as a function of sucrose concentration in C, the mean of this distribution is a sucrose concentration at which C is chosen by exactly 50 per cent of the animals. This mean concentration is taken to be isohedonic with the standard for the group of subjects as a whole.

For every point plotted in the isohedonic chart, 30 animals were tested. In a given test each rat made one and only one preferential discrimination. Incidentally, these rats were non-restricted, non-deprived, up to 20 minutes prior to testing.

The results presented in Figures 5 and 6 show isohedonic contours in the sucrose–sodium chloride area of taste. Our interpretation is that all solutions represented by points on the 1 per cent curve are equally acceptable to rats; all points on the 2 per cent curve are equally acceptable, and so forth. All points on the 2 per cent isohedon specify solutions more palatable than all points on the 1 per cent isohedon, and so on.

The open circles on these curves represent the first part of the experiment. After the entire experiment had been completed, it was replicated, and the solid circles indicate results for the second run-through. The data are highly reliable. All the second points fall within two standard errors of the first points, and most of them within one standard error of the first determinations. The order in which these curves were determined the second time was the inverse of what it was the first time, and the random orders for testing the animals differed for each test.

Let us consider the 0.5 per cent (0.086M) sodium chloride point on the 1 per cent (0.03M) sucrose isohedon. In order to equate the palatability of 0.5 per cent sodium chloride with 1 per cent sucrose, it was necessary to add approximately 0.5 per cent (0.015M) sucrose. Of course, with higher concentrations of sodium chloride, it was necessary to add more sucrose. Up to 8 per cent (1.4M) sodium chloride, however, it was possible, at least for the lower curves, to add enough sucrose to get hedonic equivalence.

This, then, concludes my discussion of our preference testing procedures and some results obtained by them.

DISCUSSION

HALPERN: If I understand you, at one-half of 1 per cent (0.086M) sodium chloride, you needed less than 1 per cent (0.03M) sucrose to match the 1 per cent. This would then suggest that you have simultaneously demonstrated a preference for sodium chloride at that concentration.

CHRISTENSEN: Yes. Kappauf is doing work with this method, and he has found that 1 per cent (0.17M) sodium chloride, contrary to the general acceptance in the literature, is equivalent to roughly 0.9 per cent (0.03M) sucrose. Heretofore, the general position held was that it was equivalent to a subthreshold sucrose. That is, the statement has been made that all sucrose solutions are superior to even the optimal sodium chloride solutions. This is not true, apparently, at least as revealed by this method.

FROMMER: How much current passed through the animals?

CHRISTENSEN: Less than ten microamps, in the neighborhood of five microamps.

HALE: Is it a capacitance-controlled relay?

CHRISTENSEN: The animal is coupled with something like 500,000 ohm resistance.

SCHEIN: Can one tie up this last isohedonic curve with the data Pilgrim presented here on sodium chloride and sucrose interactions? Perhaps Pilgrim could convert his data into an isohedonic curve.

PILGRIM: No, I would say I do not have my thinking through on it yet, although I see some possible relationships in the curve. In one sense you might look upon high sodium chloride as at least masking the preference for sucrose. We cannot say whether it masks some of the intensity, but nevertheless you must then have much more sucrose to be equivalent in the presence of a high sodium chloride concentration.

SCHEIN: How about that "dip," the enhancing effect of a little bit of sodium chloride?

CHRISTENSEN: In line with what Jacobs reported, our concern with this dip was very real, and as yet we have come up with no answer for it. Our first thought was that it really is an equal osmotic dip. We tried this, and there is no relationship at all between osmotic pressure and the dip in these curves.

PANGBORN: I think the main difference between the animal experiments just presented and the work with humans that Pilgrim and I spoke about was that with a human you do not necessarily care whether he likes a substance or not. You may simply ask him for relative intensity judgments, whereas, with the rat, whether the rat likes it or not influences the values that Christensen reported.

MORRISON: In the recent paper by Deutsch and Jones (1960), the authors spoke of diluted water as the explanation for salt preference. I hesitate to accept their interpretation. I am sure that Christensen has data related to this question. One way to test whether Deutsch's theory is correct would be this: With a two-choice situation, between water and sodium chloride, you count the number of approaches to each solution that the animal made during a long period of time (using the apparatus of Fig. 4), or you have a discrete-trial situation (e.g., the brief-exposure preference tester shown in Fig. 3). If Deutsch is correct, then the animal should go approximately 50 per cent of the time to each side. The difference in intake would come from the animal's spending more time at the sodium chloride. I doubt that the animal will do this.

CHRISTENSEN: Let me say that I firmly agree with you, and for several reasons. It is my recollection that Deutsch himself acknowledges in his article (Deutsch and Jones, 1960) that the brief-exposure preference data which indicate that the animal really does, over brief periods of time, prefer weak sodium chloride solutions to water (Young and Falk, 1956) are a very damaging blow to the theory which he proposes. Deutsch therefore dismisses these data on the basis that the animals used by Young and others had a long history of sodium deprivation and, therefore, the preference can be explained on the basis of their need state. I do not know where this idea came from, because the article as written by Young and Falk (1956) very clearly states that these animals were 90 days of age at the time of testing and were all naïve animals that had never been on anything other than an *ad libitum* schedule. This, coupled with the dip in the curves, is, I think, very clear evidence for the preference for salt.

HALPERN: It seems to me that the dip in your curve which shows that there is a preference for sodium chloride under conditions where it is unlikely that the rat is fulfilling a water deficit by taking in the saline directly controverts Deutsch's data. It would seem reasonable for somebody to try a direct replication of his experiment with water-satiated rats in the T-maze and see if they will choose between water and sodium chloride.

CHRISTENSEN: Should Deutsch's results prove to be correct, and I have no reason to believe that they might not, it would not present any serious criticism of our data, simply because the methodology which one uses to indicate preference very clearly determines the nature of the data obtained. Some years ago, Young and I tried to get this summative effect using the old discrete-trial preference tester and found only very poor indications of the summative effect. This indicates, at least to us, that this apparatus does not give precise enough or fine enough discrimination of data. Therefore, it does not seem extremely unreasonable to me that the same thing might be said of Deutsch's apparatus.

PANGBORN: It has been our observation with highly trained human subjects that 0.04M (1.4 per cent) reagent-grade lactose can be distinguished from distilled water by smell alone. Commercial sucrose has a distinct, characteristic odor, also. Since the sense of smell is generally thought to be more highly developed in animals than in humans, is it possible that choices made by experimental animals are largely influenced by odor rather than by taste?

BENJAMIN: In the course of doing some quinine hydrochloride discrimination experiments with brain-operated rats, using two different types of measures of discrimination—one, the usual preference technique and the other, a shock avoidance method—we found that rats can smell quinine hydrochloride at concentrations lower than they can taste it.

KITCHELL: Does distilled water smell?

PANGBORN: The distilled water available to our laboratory has an odor and a taste. Therefore, we double-distilled tap water so that it was relatively odorless and tasteless. The human olfactory system is approximately ten times more sensitive to flavors than is the sense of taste.

JACOBS: What adjectives did the human panel use to describe the odors of sugars?

PANGBORN: The panel said the sucrose smelled dirty, musty, or burnt.

Lactose smells sweet and aromatic. We suffer from a lack of adequate descriptive terminology in this field.

ENGEN: I should like to get these two papers together on an important general problem, relating to the discussion Jacobs and Fishman had in the previous session about where to implant the electrode.

It seems to me that, when you use a human subject, you have one very important advantage: the subject speaks your language. You do not have the problem of anthropomorphic interpretation. The human subject can tell you, or at least you can ask him, either for a preference or for only a discrimination. You cannot do that easily with animals. Sometimes such an animal experiment is called a preference experiment, sometimes a discrimination experiment. One is most likely to describe the results of the experiment with words like "threshold," which in the old categories of psychology belong in studies of discrimination rather than motivation. I would suggest that we consider this problem of discrimination or sensation versus preference or motivation.

CHRISTENSEN: I think the distinction can be made in the case of animal work. That is, it is possible, with shock avoidance techniques or something of this nature, to distinguish between discrimination and preference. I think the point which you are building up to is that it is very important that we be well aware of the differences between the two, and I agree with this wholeheartedly.

KARE: In connection with what has been discussed, Pick carried out an experiment with chickens in which he conditioned them to 2 per cent (0.34M) sodium chloride. If they were presented with 2 per cent sodium chloride, they pecked at the water at least 16 times and ran over and got their reward; if it was ordinary water, they just pecked a single time. Once he had them conditioned, he started reducing the concentration until it was very low. He thought perhaps they were smelling the salt, but they were not. They could see the small imperfections in the plastic waterers. It might be better to recheck the smelling of that sucrose and see if the subjects were not seeing it.

KITCHELL: How did you know that they were seeing the imperfections?

KARE: Pick was using two waterers with sodium chloride and two others with water. Once they were conditioned, he wanted to find out the minimum concentration they could perceive. Since the concentrations effective were so low, he checked his methods. He found that by just changing the containers (in fact, merely the detachable base of the containers) after washing them out, their response was independent of what solution was in them. The chickens had become conditioned to the two containers that originally had salt, and he could get them to respond depending on which container he presented, with or without salt. Incidentally, the birds seemed to be just putting their beaks in the water and not drinking at all.

HALE: How do you define a satiated rat?

CHRISTENSEN: We sidestepped this problem by calling them non-deprived animals rather than satiated rats.

HALE: Is it possible to have a truly non-deprived animal?

CHRISTENSEN: If we define non-deprived the way we define it.

HALE: I am not trying to quibble. There is a relevant consideration I wish to emphasize. Although Beach and Jordan (1956; Beach, 1956) speak of sexual satiation, in our work with bulls Almquist and I find we must define satiation in terms of highly specific stimulus conditions (Hale and Almquist, 1960). Do we need to do the same thing to some degree in dealing with food intake, or may we continue to think of a general satiety?

GOLDSTEIN: Satiation or non-deprivation in hunger usually means that the animal, any time he wants to, can find food or water in its environment. One could define it the same way in sex behavior. That is, if you kept males and females together, this would be analogous to non-deprivation or satiation. Ordinarily, of course, one does not. In rearing animals with the sexes apart in the standard laboratory situation, you have set up a deprivation condition.

HALE: I agree. However, we find that bulls having continuous access to females must be considered deprived to some degree since the addition of new females leads to extensive sexual responses to the new animals. Presenting familiar females in a new situation also increases sexual responses of bulls to them.

GOLDSTEIN: I think you might find the same phenomenon in food.

DILGER: I am working on the behavior of the parrot genus *Agapornis* (Dilger, 1960). If nest material is left in the cages at all times, the birds prepare and carry a certain amount every day. However, if fresh material is added, the birds then prepare and carry much more than they would have otherwise. These birds act as though they had been deprived relative to nesting material, but what they may have been deprived of is opportunity to exercise their apparently rather strong "curiosity drive." The same behavior is apparent when fresh water or food is put in their cages, or anything else for that matter. Satiation and need are, of course, quite different things.

JACOBS: I do not see the problem in defining satiation: this is when things stop. It is more difficult perhaps to define deprivation, at least in a physiological sense.

HALE: The problem is one of specifying the conditions under which things stop. Let me suggest one example, a classic one. A chicken may stop eating but starts again if a hungry chicken is placed with it.

JACOBS: The work you refer to was described by Katz (1953). I've never seen the quantitative results, but I doubt very much that the chicken would become obese this way in any sense of the term. I believe that simple environmental determination of food intake would asymptote much more quickly than sex would in Hale's experiments.

BENJAMIN: Welker has been working on this problem (Welker, 1960). He calls it the effect of novelty. Recently he has been working on various taste substances, or at least substances which can be chewed, by taking two standard rat diets. Having the animals for a week on one diet and then switching to the other will increase food consumption tremendously, and this happens with all sorts of substances—erasers, crayons, everything, so that I think when an animal is satiated is a very broad question.

HALPERN: Perhaps a distinction ought to be made between a satiated animal and a need-free animal. As Jacobs said, a satiated animal is the one who has stopped taking that which is available to him under a particular set of conditions. You cannot conclude from this that if you give him something else he will not take some of it. All you can say is that he is not taking any of the things that are offered to him. Then, if you put him in another situation and he starts taking them again, you might say he is selecting objects for which he is satiated, but the long series of exploratory behavior experiments (Dember, 1956) and reinforcement effects of changing environment (Stewart, 1960) clearly show that almost any kind of a change will be reinforcing for the rat.

HALE: You bring us exactly to the point I was interested in—a need-free animal.

FROMMER: The question here of course is the nature of the criterion. I heard a gastrointestinal physiologist describe work showing that the criterion is a very important thing in terms of what a balanced diet is. If you mean how heavy an animal is and how fast he grows, then you have to talk about one diet; but if you talk about reproductive success, then you have to talk about a different diet. If you talk about longevity, then this is a third diet; so your criterion for these is very subtle and very important.

CHAPTER 5

Metabolic and Taste Interactions

Jay Tepperman

WHEN I WAS ASSIGNED the topic of taste, metabolism, and nutrition, I did not know what to do with it. After I had been looking at these three words for some time as a sort of verbal Rorschach-test inkblot, they began to arrange themselves into the patterns shown in Figure 1.

In the pattern designated "A" (Fig. 1), there is some sort of physiologic modification of metabolism and then a nutritional adaptation, presumably with the participation of taste or other discriminating sense —odor, perhaps. This is one general pattern in which taste, metabolism, and nutrition can be related to one another. In type "B," which is really very similar to type "A," the primary difficulty is a nutritional deficiency of some sort which gives rise to a metabolic defect. This is communicated to appropriate tissues in some way, so that by means of taste a nutritional adaptation to deficiency might be achieved. Type "C" simply represents an inversion and rescrambling of the familiar words. It is easy to understand how taste might very well help to determine what we define as the "metabolic mixture," which is the mixture of foodstuffs presented to the tissues for metabolism. The nature of the metabolic mixture in turn can result in metabolic adaptation—a modification of the metabolism of the tissue in the direction of more efficient oxidation of this metabolic mixture. On the other hand, the nature of the metabolic mixture might result in a predisposition to disease. When I contemplated this outline, I was extremely embarrassed to discover that the only constructive contributions to the discussion that I can make from my personal experience are related to area "C." I confess that most of my information having to do with areas "A" and "B" is from Richter's well-known studies (Richter, 1943).

In one typical food-choice experiment Richter showed that pancreatectomy was followed by a sharp decrease in the ingestion of sugar and an increase in the amount of olive oil consumed by the animal (Richter and Schmidt, 1941). In another (Richter, 1942), an animal was given progressively larger amounts of insulin over a period of days, and it was also given access to 50 per cent dextrose solution. As the animal got more and more hypoglycemic, it ingested more and more of this sugar solution. Most interesting of all, when the insulin injections were abruptly stopped, the animal practically stopped taking the sugar. This change in selection is rather reminiscent of the first experiment, because it is fairly well known that insulin injections of this sort will lower the insulin content of the pancreas and will indeed induce a transitory diabetes. Here we have a very beautiful example of what looks to me like the sort of thing that Richter has called environmental homeostasis: a participation of sense in the orienting of the individual in its environment.

In a third experiment animals were given access to calcium lactate

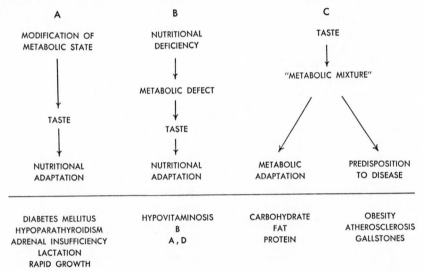

Fig. 1.—Patterns showing interrelations of taste, metabolism, and nutrition. Examples discussed in the text are shown below the line.

and water on a choice basis (Richter and Eckert, 1937). The rate of calcium lactate ingestion was fairly low. Subsequent to the removal of the parathyroid gland, there was a sharp increase in the amount of calcium solution that these animals drank. When parathyroid gland was implanted, there was a regression of the calcium lactate ingestion and an increase in the water ingestion. This is somewhat reminiscent of the women in the West Indies who, when they become pregnant, eat the chalk with which they chalk their looms.

Similarly, when an animal is given access to sodium chloride and adrenalectomy is performed, an increase in sodium chloride consumption is observed. (It is rather interesting that this also happens in the clinical counterpart of this condition—Addison's disease. Addisonians are notoriously salt-hungry and salt their food very vigorously before they taste it [Wilkins and Richter, 1940].) Adrenalectomized rats were unable to increase their salt consumption when the glossopharyngeal, chorda tympani, and lingual nerves were cut (Richter, 1939). Here I think we have reasonably direct evidence that the sensation of taste is involved in the ability to make this kind of adaptation. In all these circumstances the sequence of events appears to be consistent with the pattern we have designated as "A."

Examples of pattern "B" can also be found in the work of the Richter school. For instance, a vitamin B deficiency induced a preference for oil and a comparative rejection of sugar (Richter, 1943). Teleologically, these were "wise" choices since thiamine is particularly involved in the metabolism of sugar. Similarly, riboflavin deficiency was associated with comparative rejection of casein, and repair of this deficiency was associated with a rise in casein and oil consumption and a fall in sugar consumption (Richter, 1943). Here the primary triggering event appeared to be related to a missing dietary component and the subsequent correction of a deficiency.

We have dispensed very briskly with "A" and "B," and now we come to "C." It is very well known that the metabolic mixture, the composition of the diet, enormously modifies metabolism. A repetition of an old experiment was done by our medical students as part of their laboratory projects during one year. If rats are given isocaloric high fat and high carbohydrate diets and glucose tolerance curves are done on them, the carbohydrate-diet animals have a glucose tolerance curve which is characterized by rapid disappearance of glucose from the blood, whereas the high-fat-diet animals have really a rather typically diabetic type of glucose tolerance curve, a physiologic kind of diabetes, so to speak. The carbohydrate-diet animals are distinctly more sensitive to a standard test dose of insulin than the fat-diet animals are, and this I think represents a true consequence of tissue adaptations to a change in metabolic mixture, which could be determined initially by taste preference.

Adaptations to metabolic mixtures can be extraordinarily acute. For example, if three serial glucose injections are given at intervals of three hours, there is a progressive improvement in glucose tolerance, i.e., there is a decrease in the peak glucose concentration in the blood and an increase in rate of glucose removal with successive doses of glucose. This has often been referred to as the Hamman-Hirschman effect (Hamman and Hirschman, 1919), or the Staub-Traugott phenomenon.

The mechanism that may be involved in this acute adaptation is the acute "training" of the lipogenic apparatus in this circumstance. It is now well recognized that the shift to high carbohydrate metabolic mixtures is accompanied by an increased capacity for transforming glucose and glucose intermediates to long-chain fatty acids, both in liver and in adipose tissue. If, as has been postulated, the lipogenic capacity of the tissues mentioned is limited by the availability of reduced triphosphopyridine nucleotide (TPNH) at high rates of lipogenesis, the oxidation of more and more glucose via the hexosemonophosphate shunt would supply increasing amounts of TPNH and thus facilitate the conversion of glucose to fatty acids. Thus, the more glucose the cell uses, the more efficient the cell becomes at disposing of it by way of fat formation. If the original shift toward glucose involved taste, this would be an example of a profound indirect effect of taste on metabolism. Those interested in a detailed consideration of adaptive hyperlipogenesis are referred to a recent essay on the subject (Tepperman and Tepperman, 1958).

Here is an example from the field of lipid metabolism. Isocaloric high fat and high carbohydrate diets were fed to rats, and then liver slices

TABLE 1

OXIDATION OF PALMITIC ACID 1-C^{14} BY LIVER SLICES OF
CARBOHYDRATE- AND FAT-DIET-ADAPTED RATS*

Diet	Body Wt. (Gm.)	Liver Nitrogen (Per Cent of Wet Wt.)	Liver Fat (Per Cent of Wet Wt.)	Q_{O_2} Representative Dry Wt.	Specific Activity of CO_2 (Counts/Min/ mg $BaCO_3$)
Carbohydrate..	369.3 ± 11.8	2.93 ± 0.05	5.6 ± 0.18	5.3 ± 0.16	277.5 ± 14.6
Fat..........	400.1 ± 11.2	3.02 ± 0.02	9.1 ± 0.65	5.1 ± 0.18	517.1 ± 30.2
P............	$>.3$	$>.3$	$<.01$	$>.3$	$<.01$

*Each flask contained 2.6 ml. buffered emulsion with final concentrations .0009M unlabeled glucose and .004M palmitate 1-C^{14} having 112,500 total counts/min. Approximately 175-mg. liver slices were used in each vessel Incubation time was 2 hr. Means with standard errors are given for each measurement.

from these animals were incubated *in vitro* in the presence of C^{14}-labeled palmitic acid. The rate of catabolism of the palmitic acid was estimated from the radioactivity in the respiratory CO_2. Liver slices from the high-fat-diet animals catabolized significantly more of the palmitic acid *in vitro* than did the slices from the carbohydrate-fed animals (see Table 1). The next part of the experiment was suggested by the work of Lundbaek and Stevenson (1948) and by that of others. These workers studied the metabolism of surviving diaphragm muscle obtained from carbohydrate- and fat-diet-adapted rats. In spite of the fact that the rate of oxygen consumption of the diaphragms from the two sets of animals was precisely the same, the abstraction of glucose from the buffer by the diaphragms of the high fat-diet animals was significantly less than the abstraction of glucose from the buffer by the diaphragms of the high carbohydrate animals. In addition to this, we added radioactive palmitic acid to the same vessels, and we got a significant increase in the rate of disappearance of the labeled fatty acid by the muscles obtained from high fat-diet-adapted animals. In these muscles there had been a reorganization of the metabolic machinery in such a way as to accommodate the high fat diet (Tepperman *et al.*, 1956). This is the type of thing that happens in tissues in response to changes in metabolic mixtures (see Table 2).

An example of the same sort of thing from the field of protein metabolism is an experiment by Mandelstam and Yudkin (1952). They measured the enzyme, arginase, which is crucially concerned in the metabolism of the amino acid arginine, in the livers of three different groups of animals: 20 per cent dietary protein, 40 per cent dietary protein, and 60 per cent dietary protein. They showed a marked variation in hepatic arginase activity that was related to the amount of protein the animal had been forced to eat. This can be viewed as a

TABLE 2

OXIDATION OF PALMITIC ACID 1-C^{14} BY DIAPHRAGMS OF
CARBOHYDRATE- AND FAT-DIET-ADAPTED RATS*

Diet	Body Wt. (Gm.)	Q_{O_2} Representative Dry Wt.	Radioactivity in CO_2 (Counts/Min/mg $BaCO_3$)	μg. Glucose Abstracted/mg Dry Wt.
Carbohydrate.......	347.9 ± 10.2	4.2 ± 0.34	754.9 ± 36.2	10.4 ± 0.46
Fat...............	364.1 ± 16.0	4.2 ± 0.17	948.2 ± 43.1	7.8 ± 0.37
P................	$> .3$	$> .3$	$< .01$	$< .01$

*Warburg flasks each contained 2.6 ml. buffered emulsion with substrate concentrations .006M unlabeled glucose and .008M palmitate 1-C^{14}, having 225,000 total counts/min, and approximately 200 mg. diaphragm. Incubation time was 2 hr. Means and standard errors are given for 7 carbohydrate-fed and 9 fat-fed rats (glucose levels for 5 and 6, respectively).

sort of "work hypertrophy" of the hepatic arginase. It is not definitely known that this is *de novo* enzyme synthesis, but the inference is pretty strong that it is. These same workers did a nice experiment in which they attempted this type of adaptation in very young weanling animals that were rapidly growing and again in plateaued animals. They showed that the intensity of response in the young rapidly growing animal is very much greater than it was in the plateaued animal, and I think, therefore, that we can be satisfied for the moment that this actually represents an eliciting of new enzyme by the demands that are placed on it by the metabolic situation, and again this could go back to taste preference.

We used to think that obesity was very simple; in fact, we used to call it simple obesity; but we do not think it is very simple any more. Largely as the result of the work of Brobeck, Anand, Hetherington, and many others (Brobeck, 1946), we are very much interested in the whole complex of structures in the hypothalamus which function to regulate food intake. Whether or not obesity happens is the resultant of a very large number of interconnected variables and many environmental factors playing on them (see Fig. 2). We always must stop whenever we talk about things like this and pay our respects to the new icon, the Watson and Crick model of the desoxyribose nucleic acid (DNA) molecule, because we think that heredity is very centrally involved in this condition. Mayer (1953) and his group and others have shown how important genetic factors are in the development of obesity, at least in some animals. The hedonistic aspects of taste referred to in previous talks play a tremendously important role in the development of obesity, because there are people who use the hedonistic aspect of taste in the same way that other people use whatever it is that alcohol does to you, and they become obese. This is one way in which taste participates in the problem of obesity.

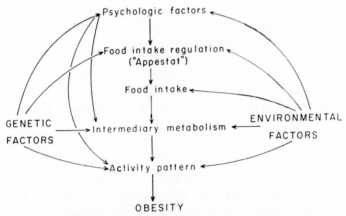

Fig. 2.—Schematic representation of some of the interconnected variables and complex factors which may interact to produce obesity.

There is an experiment of Dwight Ingle's in which he had animals maintained in very limited space as compared with other animals that were able to move around a little bit more. He fed these animals a sucrose-containing, high-fat liquid diet. The food intake regulatory equipment they had could not stand up to this kind of situation. Some of his rats attained weights of over a kilogram. This is an example, I think, of the participation of taste in the causing of a disease.

It is well known that there are dietary factors involved in the etiology of atherosclerosis. I submit that taste and discriminatory sense generally could very well participate in this in an indirect way by influencing the nature of the metabolic mixture and by setting up a circumstance in which this disease could occur in conjunction with all other favorable (or unfavorable) conditions. I do not think that this is the time or the place to go into a discussion of the role of cholesterol in the genesis of atherosclerosis, or whether or not one should eat corn oil margarine. The point is that this is a prototype of a whole constellation of diseases which seem to be very closely related to the metabolic mixture, which is, to a certain extent, established by taste.

There is another very recent example of a disease caused by modification of the metabolic mixture, in this case a miniature model of a widespread human disease. Some months ago, in the course of a study of serum cholesterol concentrations in obese and lean animals, we placed mice on a cholesterol, cholic acid, low protein, and high fat diet. When the mice were autopsied after eight months on the regimen, nine out of ten of them had gallstones which, on analysis, proved to be practically reagent-grade cholesterol. Such stones are never seen in animals on ordinary laboratory rations. Now we have a model of an important human disease, and it will be possible to study in some detail the conditions under which cholesterol stone formation occurs in bile. This is another example of a disease which is due, in part, to a modification of the metabolic mixture, and which, therefore, could be influenced by congenital or acquired taste.

In summary, a number of interrelations among taste, metabolism, and nutrition have been discussed and specific examples of each pattern have been cited. A graphic summary of the discussion is given in Figure 1.

DISCUSSION

JACOBS: I would like to comment on the pancreatectomy. Richter found, as you pointed out, that the animals increased fat intake, decreased carbohydrate intake, and initially, as he put it, "cured themselves" (Richter and Schmidt, 1941). In the long run, of course, this diet would kill the animal; thus the animals were not really acting efficiently, at least from the current points of view. Both Soulairac (1947) and I, later (Jacobs, 1955), tried this with alloxan diabetic animals. We find that an alloxan diabetic animal loves glucose and will take even more than animals that are given insulin (Jacobs, 1958). This would appear, superficially, to be in contradiction to Richter's work but is difficult to interpret. Alloxan produces specific beta cell destruction. Successful pancreatectomy also removes enzyme sources important in fat metabolism. It is possible that Richter's increase in fat intake may be related to this source, i.e., a pancreatectomy-induced need for fat. I have observed another interesting phenomenon on the alloxan diabetic animals that I have used: I have tried giving them fructose because of the plentiful comments on the efficacy of using fructose in the treatment of diabetes. They do not like it at all.

Insulin has been a classic factor in the study of hunger because it increases general caloric intake. Richter (1942) and Soulairac (1950) have shown that insulin also increases the carbohydrate portion of the diet when the animal is given a choice. If you narrow the choice even more and give a choice between two glucose solutions, the naïve animal to whom insulin injections have been given will temporarily switch preference to the sweeter of the two solutions. I decided to use a fructose solution to see if the rat would still go to the sweeter solution, even if that solution did not do as much good. We cannot ask a rat how sweet fructose is, but we can measure impulses in the chorda tympani, and by these results fructose is sweeter (Hagstrom, E. C., pers. comm.). When you offer 30 per cent (1.7M) fructose and glucose solutions, the animal will temporarily take fructose over glucose even though the fructose is inferior in alleviating the symptoms of hypoglycemia.

TEPPERMAN: This is taking the fructose by mouth?

JACOBS: Yes. This is a very transient effect. I have only been able to show it for twelve hours in my experiments.

TEPPERMAN: It seems to me that if fructose is absorbed in the gastro-intestinal tract and goes to the liver, it shows up in the blood stream as glucose, and, therefore, you could hope that it would, to a certain extent, help to alleviate the hypoglycemia.

JACOBS: Yes. I do not know that I could argue that fructose has zero efficiency. All I am arguing is that, unless 100 per cent of the initial load of fructose is converted in the liver, it is not going to do as much. The early work on administering different sugars to animals in hypoglycemic convulsions indicated that fructose was not as effective as glucose (Bhattacharya *et al.*, 1951; Davis *et al.*, 1960; Geiger *et al.*, 1954; Herring *et al.*, 1924; Klein *et al.*, 1946).

As you give the animal a more specific choice, you can perhaps find out a little bit more about what the animal is regulating for, from the physiological point of view. The relation between insulin and specific hunger is difficult to interpret from the point of view of the glucostatic theory of general hunger, as it is currently developed. I would speculate that caloric deficits, whichever way you induce them, may always produce specific hungers. I am not suggesting that there is no such thing as a general hunger or that we really have to assume that all animals behave under all conditions as the adrenalectomized one does, but I am suggesting that giving animals choices may give you some hints as to where to go physiologically. It would be nice to be able to make some assumptions about how changes in carbohydrate metabolism can produce specific choices as well as an increase in caloric intake.

Adrenalectomy is a beautiful paradigm of Tepperman's example "A." Much work has been done on adrenalectomy in terms of relating salt efficiency to salt hunger. Over the past several years, a group of physiologists have begun to analyze the opposite case: Salt avoidance in hypertension, presumably related to salt retention. The initial studies were done at Harvard (Tosteson *et al.*, 1951). They were systematically followed up by Fregly. He induced experimental hypertension in rats by chronic kidney encapsulation and found that these animals avoided NaCl (Fregly, 1956). Further studies showed this to be a general cation avoidance (Fregly, 1959). Hypertension is pretty complex and salt retention is only one factor in it.

TEPPERMAN: This brings up a question that I would like to hear some discussion about. The whole business of regulation of fluid and electrolyte balance in the body gets more and more complicated week by week. The point that I was wondering about was this: We know a little bit about the structures in the brain that have to do with osmoreception and therefore are probably very intimately related to salt and water balance. Until two weeks ago we thought there was a place in the brain that regulated the adrenal salt-retaining hormone. Since the last endocrine meetings in Miami, I do not suppose we are sure (Davis *et al.*, 1960). There have been described in the brain discrete locations which participate in these regulations. The question I would like to ask is: Is it possible that these very structures participate in a complicated response like cation avoidance or selection in some way? The regulatory structures are somehow or other connected in an informational way with what it is that makes the animal compensate for his deficit by drinking salt water.

JACOBS: There have been a series of experiments by Stellar (Stellar *et al.*, 1954), O'Kelly (O'Kelly and Falk, 1958), and others, showing that stomach loads of hypertonic salt solutions do tend to shift the preference curve for salt solutions. Thus, it would seem that by changing the peripheral information available to the animal, you can change salt intake.

TITLEBAUM: I can add a comment on your studies with reference to salt thresholds. This is an experiment that we recently completed (Titlebaum *et al.*, 1960), in which diabetes insipidus rats were tested with various NaCl solutions. Such rats have less tolerance to salt loads than normals (Swann and Penner, 1939). The diabetes insipidus animal can be considered to have increased Na extracellularly (Friedman *et al.*, 1958). It was found that serum sodium remains unchanged, but the extracellular fluid expands approximately 5 per cent isotonically, i.e., a greater *total* amount of Na is contained in the extracellular fluid. We gave salt preference tests to these animals and found a shift toward the hypotonic end of the salt preference-aversion curve which is similar to what would occur if normal animals had been previously loaded with salt solutions or dehydrated. If the major internal environmental determinant of NaCl solution intake were serum Na concentration, then the acceptance-rejection function of diabetes insipidus and normal rats would be similar, since serum Na is unchanged in diabetes insipidus. Here, then, some other internal factor is operating against the acceptance of NaCl solutions, which are poorly tolerated by the diabetes insipidus rat when it is given stomach loads of these solutions.

HALE: Here we have considerable beautiful evidence of the regulation of intake to bring about a nutritional adaptation in the case of a metabolic shift or in the case of some actual deficiency. There are several of you here who have been interested in how taste regulates these.

FROMMER: There is the experiment by Pfaffmann and Bare (1950), observing chorda tympani response thresholds to sodium chloride solutions in normal and adrenalectomized animals. They were able to detect no difference at this point in the gustatory system. The great dream is to have chronic implants in the thalamus and to do the same kind of experiment, to see whether you can get a modification at this level of the nervous system.

TEPPERMAN: Is there any possibility that the taste end-organs could function as monitors of the concentrations of critical materials in the body fluids and thus participate in this kind of thing?

HALPERN: I think that one can, on a logical basis, reject this for taste end-organs in the tongue. I talked about this with Visek of the University of Chicago. He made a logical analysis of the problem: The "sodium chloride" concentration in the blood is about tenth molar (0.55 per cent). Tenth molar sodium chloride applied to the tongue of a rat or a human is a very effective stimulus. If the blood and the topical application were being monitored by the same mechanism, the receptor should be completely adapted to 0.1 molar sodium chloride. If this logic is correct, then the taste buds, per se, would generally not be monitors of body fluid content. It is true, of course, that people are said to taste drugs when these are injected intravenously. Hagstrom has been working on this problem for some time. He has found that intravenous injections of common sapid substances, with the possible exception of saccharin, do not produce chorda tympani impulses. Drug-like substances such as nicotinic acid and desoxycholic acid are effective (Hagstrom, E. C. Gustatory nerve responses to intravenous injection of chemicals. Unpublished data).

An additional line of evidence is the intravenous reinforcement learning experiments reported by Chambers (Coppock and Chambers, 1954; Chambers, 1956a). No learning occurred with normal saline injection.

HARRIMAN: I would like to comment with respect to the possibility that taste may serve as a monitor. Young and Chaplin (1949) have reported that groups of normal or adrenalectomized rats took in more total sodium when a range of concentrations, rather than only 3 per cent (0.5M) was offered in a group cafeteria-feeding situation. (The interpretation of this experiment is complicated by the report of Edmonds [1960*a*] that 2 per cent [0.34M] NaCl is toxic for adrenalectomized rats.)

Perhaps there is another way of looking at this matter of taste, one which is alternative to the teleological approach advanced by Tepperman and Jacobs. I have never been quite able to sympathize with teleology, perhaps because of its *ad hoc* nature. The possibility does exist that taste may serve here as a discriminating stimulus and as a secondary reinforcer. Is it not possible that physiological benefit is derived, and the taste is simply a cue that primary reinforcement will follow? For example, cod liver oil may be quite acceptable at one time in the life of an individual simply because of the tremendous amount of reinforcing value that the substance has, and, when this value is lost, the taste changes.

TEPPERMAN: That sounds teleological to me.

HALPERN: The reinforcing value, per se, is determined operationally on the basis of what the organism does. If he takes in more of the substance or exerts more effort to get it, it is a reinforcer. You have not defined the term independently of the operations you are using for measuring it.

TEPPERMAN: I think the difficulty with getting into discussions of teleological reasoning in biology is that there are a whole lot of unwanted connotations of the word which really have nothing to do with the use of teleological thinking in the biological situation. A lot of people think that as soon as you admit the idea of teleology you have to become some sort of practicing religionist. This has nothing to do with teleology in the sense in which I am using the word.

HARRIMAN: Kare referred earlier to chickens given thiamin-depleted diets and pointed out how they became anorexic in a very short time, but how, when they were given thiamin hydrochloride, they began to eat. Now, I suppose there is a teleological explanation here, but one can also say that perhaps thiamin produces very, very quick benefit. The physiological deficit is very quickly made up. There might be a great possibility of short-time learning.

KARE: Wood-Gush, while here at Cornell, did a study on specific hunger for calcium. He depleted the birds of calcium and then tested their ability to select the calcium-adequate diet in a two-choice situation. They did select the calcium-adequate diet but rejected a strontium replacement. The results varied depending upon which calcium salt he used. I think one of the difficulties here is that results obtained depend upon the circumstances under which you test the specific hunger. I think it unwise to lump the consideration of salt together with vitamins or with sugar. The body of the animal may employ entirely different mechanisms to cope with each of these deficiency situations.

In the case of the calcium deprivation, those birds that were deprived behaved very differently from those who were not deprived. The deficient animals showed less fear of the experimenter and demonstrated intensive exploratory pecking at any object available. In any event, an animal deprived of calcium given two choices, one with a specific calcium salt, has the capacity to select the diet that will correct its deficiency.

HARRIMAN: This is what I meant by the *ad hoc* nature of this manner of approach. If an animal corrects a nutritional deficiency through appropriate dietary choice, it is said that it has a specific hunger for the substance chosen. If the animal does not select the substance required to reduce a nutritional need, it is said that the animal lacks a specific hunger. Perhaps the alternative approach which I mentioned earlier can generate an explanation of compensatory appetitive selection in terms of reinforcement learning. If so, then we must consider the possibility that the degree of physiological need, the distinctiveness of the flavor of the needed substance, and the delay period between the time the food is ingested and the time the food brings about some diminution of need are critically important factors. Perhaps study of these factors will permit predictions to be made as to whether or not compensatory appetitive choice will be made, and, if they are made, how long it will require for such a pattern of choice to become established in the depleted animal.

KARE: That is possible, except that a bird will kill itself on galactose even where it has a choice to avoid it. Evidently there the internal well-being can be ignored.

Metabolic Factors in Food Intake and Utilization in Weanling Rats

Franklin W. Heggeness

T HE EXPERIMENTS I wish to discuss are concerned with a specific instance in which some nutritional and metabolic factors influence food intake and utilization. We usually consider the metabolic requirements of an animal, including such things as the degree of activity, to be significant in regulating the magnitude of the caloric intake. The results of the experiments to be described here are consistent with the conclusion that, in the case of weanling animals fed high carbohydrate diets, calories in excess of requirements are ingested. It was found that these animals develop a transient, self-limiting elevation in metabolism. The metabolic rate is elevated approximately 20 per cent above predicted values for the first week of feeding. The results of further studies of this metabolic response suggest that it is associated with a limited capacity for lipogenesis. The ingestion of calories in excess of capacity for utilization appears to lead to the calorigenic response. Preliminary evidence suggests that the carbohydrate in the diet as it influences the intake may affect the magnitude of the metabolic rate.

Weanling, Holtzman-strain animals were housed in a room maintained at a constant temperature. Water was provided *ad libitum*. Food, except during periods of caloric restriction, was always available in double food cups. The basic diet contained 60 per cent glucose, 21 per cent casein, 14 per cent fat (Crisco), four per cent salts, plus a complete vitamin supplement. Oxygen consumptions were measured on quiet, fed animals by determining the rate of volume change of a closed system containing soda lime (Watts and Gourley, 1953). Metabolic rate is expressed as liters of oxygen/hr/kg$^{.75}$.

Weanling rats fed a commercial pellet diet containing 57 per cent carbohydrate were found to have an oxygen consumption of approximately one liter/hr/kg$^{.75}$. Figure 3 shows the metabolic rate measured daily for the first six days of feeding. This is approximately 10 per cent above the basal level reported for animals of this age and comparable also to the oxygen consumptions of older animals fed any of a variety of diets. In contrast, the feeding of the 60 per cent glucose diet was found to be associated with a significant elevation in oxygen consumption. The third graph in Figure 3 shows the response usually observed; the highest elevations in metabolism occurred between days one and three. The second graph in Figure 3, showing a still greater elevation in oxygen consumption during days four to six, was observed in one of four groups. Oxygen consumption measurements after six days were not different, regardless of the diet fed.

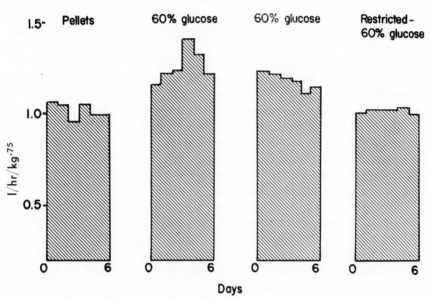

FIG. 3.—Oxygen consumption of weanling rats fed various diets

The metabolic rate was found to be unchanged three hours after initial feeding. In 18 hours, maximum rises, as shown in Figure 3, were present. The metabolism determinations were usually carried out in the morning but, when elevated, oxygen consumptions remained high throughout the day and after, up to 12 hours of fasting.

Comparable transient elevations in oxygen consumption occurred with diets containing 60 per cent of other carbohydrates. The greatest elevations occurred with the dextrin diet; glucose was the next most effective. Rats ingesting a 60 per cent starch diet showed a comparable response, but the initial rise did not occur for 24 hours; this delay may be related to the time required for these animals to ingest significant amounts of this diet. When the glucose in the diet was elevated to 70 per cent, average intake was less than that of rats fed the 60 per cent glucose diet. Oxygen consumptions of the animals fed a 70 per cent glucose diet fluctuated between 1.00 and 1.38 1/hr/kg.[75]. That the daily intake of the diet plays a role in the magnitude of the calorigenic response is suggested by the finding that the spikes in oxygen consumption of animals fed the 70 per cent diet were preceded by significant elevations in daily food intake. The acceptability of the diet as modified by the type of carbohydrate may be a factor in the magnitude of the calorigenic response. That it is the carbohydrate—not fat and protein—that plays the major role in metabolic response is suggested by the finding that when the carbohydrate content of the diet is reduced to 30 per cent (and protein and fat elevated 15 per cent above that of basal diet) oxygen consumptions resembled that of the pellet-fed group. The absence of a calorigenic response in the pellet-fed groups is not clear. The relative availability of the carbohydrate in this, as compared to the prepared diets, may be of significance.

Weanling rats introduced to the 60 per cent glucose diet by feeding amounts of diet (4 gm.) just sufficient to maintain body weight showed no calorigenic response. Furthermore, no rise in oxygen consumption occurred when *ad libitum* feeding was started five days later (Fig. 3). This period of partial caloric restriction induces some type of adaptation, and I will refer to such animals as "adapted" animals. Weanling animals fed the 60 per cent glucose diet *ad libitum* at weaning are called unadapted animals.

Fasting was found not to be an adequate stimulus for adaptation. Partial adaptation is achieved by three days of restricted feeding, but six days is necessary to obtain the maximum degree of adaptation.

The finding that a period of partial restriction abolished the calorigenic effect enabled us to compare the responses of adapted and unadapted animals both ingesting the identical diet *ad libitum*. All comparative measurements were carried out during *ad libitum* feeding. The adapted animals were subjected to six days of partial caloric restriction.

Adapted animals were found to have a superior rate of weight gain (Fig. 4). Two factors, an initially greater caloric intake and more efficient food utilization, are responsible for this. Food utilization measurements were carried out in three-day periods, thus providing a time interval adequate for reliable measurements. Adapted animals ingested 28.8 ± 1.2 gm. during the first and second three-day period of *ad libitum* feeding. Unadapted animals, on the other hand, increased their intake from 19.9 ± 0.7 to 26.8 ± 1.2 from the first to second period. Consistent with the finding that a portion of the calories ingested by the unadapted animals is required to maintain an elevated metabolism, the efficiency of food utilization for weight gain was less in this group than that in the adapted group. Adapted animals gained

0.86 ± 0.03 gm. body weight/gm food during the first three days and 0.76 ± 0.05 gm. from the fourth to sixth day. Unadapted animals gained 0.71 gm. body weight/gm of food during both three-day periods. The finding that food efficiency of the unadapted animals is unchanged during these first two periods suggests that the decrease in the calorigenic response during days four to six (Fig. 3) just counterbalances the increased energy requirements due to increase in body size. Significant differences in efficiency of utilization are also found when dry weight gains alone were considered.

When nitrogen balance studies were carried out on these two groups, no difference was found in the amount of nitrogen retained. The greater intake of the adapted animals during days one to three thus led to a significantly greater urinary excretion during the first metabolic period.

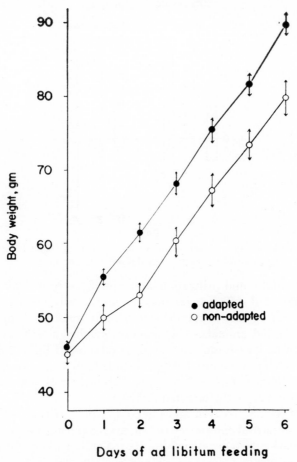

FIG. 4.—Body weight in adapted and non-adapted rats. *Arrows* indicate magnitude of standard error.

The adapted weanling animals in this study received treatment similar to adult animals "trained" by Tepperman and Tepperman (1958) to ingest their total daily intake in one hour. The animals studied by the Teppermans were found to show enhanced lipogenesis. In the studies reported here, rates of lipid accumulation were studied by carcass analysis techniques. Fat was extracted from an aliquot of dry tissue and lipid content determined gravimetrically.

During the period of caloric restriction body weights of the adapted animals remained constant. However, 50 per cent of fat originally present was replaced by water (Fig. 5). During *ad libitum* feeding,

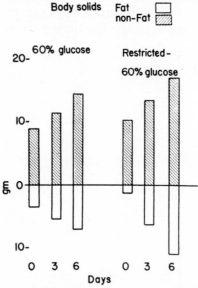

Fig. 5.—Fat and non-fat components of the body weight of adapted (restricted 60 per cent glucose) and non-adapted (60 per cent glucose) weanling rats.

when food intake and utilization were significantly greater, these animals accumulated sufficient fat to make up the initial deficit and by the sixth day their carcass contained significantly more fat than that found in the unadapted animals. The superior weight gain of these animals appeared to be largely due to this accumulation of lipid. That the rise in oxygen consumption observed in the unadapted animals is not essential for the initiation of post-weaning growth is indicated by the superior weight gains of the adapted animals.

Both the feeding pattern and the composition of the diet fed during the period of partial caloric restriction are significant factors in adaptation. Adaptation also developed in rats fed a 60 per cent fat diet during the period of partial caloric restriction. Such animals, when placed upon the 60 per cent glucose diet, showed weight gains superior to that of the unadapted animal. The rate of lipid accumulation was below that of animals fed the 60 per cent glucose diet during the adaptation but was significantly greater than that of unadapted animals. During the period of partial caloric restriction, the animals ingest their daily caloric load in less than ten minutes. If caloric balance is to be achieved, these calories must be stored and released throughout the subsequent 24 hours.

The calories ingested, aside from those required for energy requirements and growth, must be converted to glycogen and fat. If the glycogenic and lipogenic capacities are saturated, although calories are still available, a rise in metabolic rate results in a balance between expenditure and intake. This is a possible explanation for the metabolic response of the weanling rats fed high carbohydrate diets. This transient elevation in metabolism obligates approximately 15 per cent of calories ingested by the unadapted animals.

Elevations in oxygen consumption have been noted in other situations where the relative availability of calories may play a significant role. Varga (1959) measured oxygen consumption in human infants with pyloric stenosis following specific corrective surgery. During partial starvation and early periods of refeeding, the oxygen consumptions of these infants were below normal values. On the fifth day of realimentation, oxygen consumptions rose above normal values. Wierzuchowski (1937) found that the infusion of large loads of glucose into adult-trained dogs was associated with significant elevations in oxygen consumption.

The faster rate of weight gain of the adapted animals used in this study was not maintained. Between the twelfth and eighteenth day of *ad libitum* feeding, differences in body weight and composition disappeared. Preliminary studies suggest that the enhanced rate of lipid accumulation may be maintained for a longer time if these animals are subjected to alternate periods of restricted and *ad libitum* feeding. These findings raise the possibility that, if elevated lipogenic capacity is maintained, caloric intake will be increased, resulting in obesity.

DISCUSSION

JACOBS: Do you have any suggestions on how obese people might get this defect?

HEGGENESS: If one adapts an animal, feeds him for several days *ad libitum*, and then readapts him, his rate of weight gain is significantly greater than either the adapted or the non-adapted animals. As a matter of fact, their food intake is sometimes double the amount of other animals not subject to this treatment. A part of the improved weight gain of these animals is undoubtedly due to GI adaptation. The GI tracts of these "readapted" animals become tremendous when they are fed in this sort of leap-frog fashion, and I do not know yet whether it is going to be demonstrated that the capacity to form fat can be continued over any longer period of time than we have shown so far.

TEPPERMAN: I think that these are very interesting observations. They call to my mind a discussion that was raised in New Haven in about 1941 or 1942 around the ideas of a German physiologist of the 1920's called Grafe (1923), who gave this thing the name *luxus konsumption* (Kujalová and Fábry, 1960). There was a great argument about whether there was indeed anything like *luxus konsumption*. I think that you have shown pretty clearly that there is a kind of interim period between the time of the beginning of the adaptation and the time the animal learns how to throw these calories away as fat. This is certainly the way I would interpret your data.

HEGGENESS: Two things occur to me. One is that rat milk is high in fat, and this may merely represent the dietary adaptation from the high fat milk until his body is prepared to meet any kind of diet once he is weaned. I suppose the other, more philosophical, is that the animal is full of such adaptations designed to carry him from weaning to post-weaning and this may be an example of only one of them.

TEPPERMAN: Kare mentioned the problem that the calf has which starts life as a carnivore essentially and then very quickly gets turned into a herbivore. I can imagine that very similar kinds of adaptations must occur in the calf.

KARE: The point that I am concerned about in Heggeness' paper is the element of time. We have offered calves especially attractive pellets, taste-wise, and feed intake is increased above that of the controls, but it corrects itself within a month. The gain they make, they retain. However, consumption returns to that of the controls by the end of a month. If you change their diet back to the original, food intake is depressed. It takes a week for them to get over the depression. It is now common practice in agriculture in various species to use restricted feed intake. This is carried out over extended periods of time: three months, four months. The animals never compensate for missed intake, yet they consume 20 per cent less than the controls over, say, the first six months of a chicken's life. It does not adversely affect their health at all, and possibly it may even aid it.

TEPPERMAN: In the case of chickens you are not interested in longevity, but in the case of other species I think that it has been shown fairly clearly that this type of dietary restriction actually enables the animal to live a longer life. Did not McCay at Cornell do some experiments like that some years ago on systematic underfeeding?

KARE: There was a reduction in mortality with restricted feed intake; however, it was not significant (McCay *et al.*, 1935; McCay, 1958).

Recent data suggest increased mortality with restricted diet (Silberberg *et al.*, 1961). Perhaps Heggeness was taking only part of a graph, and, if he had gone on a little longer, the two lines would have come together.

HEGGENESS: Out of three such growth experiments, in one case they are still apart at 24 days, and in the other case they are together at 12 days. It seems to be largely determined by the fact that there is so much variation in ten rats that you will get a twenty-fold variation in weight, and that the two groups overlap for this reason. I think that this phenomenon is of no practical long-term consequence, and I think it is time-limited in this initial period of feeding. I would like to know if by re-stimulating this mechanism you could in this way produce a very obese animal? If one does this, the growth curve goes up rapidly and the dry weight is greater, but I do not know whether it is fat or not. A part of it is due to the increase in weight of the GI tract.

TEPPERMAN: Apropos of that are the studies of Fábry who has been doing a lot of control-feeding experiments on rats (Kujalová and Fábry, 1960). He has described the tremendous changes in the weight of the stomach, in the surface area of the absorbing part of the small intestine, the alkaline phosphatase activity of the epithelium of the small intestine, and so on. We found in 1943, when we did some of these controlled-feeding experiments, that we were able to get rats whose gastric capacity went up to 22 cc. as compared with about 5 cc. for control (Tepperman *et al.*, 1943). They were able to stow away one whole day's ration in one hour.

HEGGENESS: You also described increase in rate of absorption of carbohydrates. These animals have a gastrointestinal tract that must weigh twice as much as it does in the controls. They have a stomach into which you can almost put your fist.

I wonder if the variation in metabolic elevation that occurred could be in any way related to the acceptability of the diet. With a rat that weights only forty-five or fifty grams, to raise his metabolic rate up from 1.0 to 1.2, or 1.2 to 1.4 is about less than half a gram of this diet per day. He could lose half as much in his whiskers, and you would not notice it. I think that the magnitude of the dietary changes will be very difficult to demonstrate, but I am sure it is worth trying.

TITLEBAUM: I would like to make a comment on the ability of the animal to adapt to the diet and stress. When a mouse is injected with gold-thioglucose, it becomes obese because of lesions in the hypothalamus. In a stressful situation—for example, cold—a normal mouse will eat more in order to meet the increased energy requirements due to cold, with body weight remaining constant or even increasing slightly. A mouse who had a goldthioglucose lesion will not be able to do this; it has lost the adaptability to cold. The pre-cold rate of food intake is maintained and weight is lost as a result, so there is some kind of inter-relation there (Fregly *et al.,* 1957).

TEPPERMAN: Is he already eating at a high level when you put him in the cold?

TITLEBAUM: Yes. The goldthioglucose mouse shows an initial trend toward a decrease in eating when placed in the cold. The normal mouse may increase its food intake above that of the goldthioglucose animal, which remains at a level similar to its intake at normal room tempera-tures.

TEPPERMAN: Of course he is already eating a large enough amount of food to compensate for his cold exposure at the time you put him in. He does not have to increase his intake again.

TITLEBAUM: Probably not as much as the normal animal would have to.

HEGGENESS: Are these chemically obese mice already eating as much as they can stuff into their stomachs, or can it be increased beyond this?

TEPPERMAN: From our experience, there is a dynamic phase of the obesity, and then, when the animals get tremendously obese, their food intake comes down and approaches normal, but it is not yet down to it. At the time of the dynamic phase of the obesity, if the goldthioglucose has really hit the button, so to speak, these animals are eating enormous amounts of food as compared with their control litter mates, and it is hard for me to see how they could physically adapt to anything by in-creasing their food intake above an already tremendously elevated one. But later on, when they get into the more static phase of the obesity, it is possible to get them to overeat. Furthermore, when they get into the static phase of the obesity, you can starve them down to the weight of their normal litter mates, and then they will re-enter the dynamic phase and eat just as much as they did right after the lesion took place. This is also true of hypothalamic obesity.

TITLEBAUM: The interesting thing about it is that when they are starved down to their preoperative weight, they go into a second dynamic phase where they will eat more than they did in the first phase and regain this weight at a much faster rate than initially (Titlebaum and Falk, unpublished).

TEPPERMAN: I had not been aware of that. It suggests the possibility that they have sort of a head start on the adaptation that they have to make in order to put on all this weight.

TITLEBAUM: Could it be because their gastric capacity is larger al-ready?

HEGGENESS: In these animals which are leapfrogged, it seems that this is the case. The second time you institute *ad libitum* feeding, they gain weight faster, but their stomachs are already a third bigger than they were before, and their food consumption is much bigger.

DILGER: It occurs to me that some rather gross anatomical changes are known in birds coincident with changes of diet, but I do not know anything about the physiological changes which must also be very great. Some gulls, for instance, live part of the year along shores, mostly eating dead animals such as fish (a high protein diet), and their stomachs are essentially simple sacs. In the winter they glean fields of grain, becoming herbivores, and now their stomachs are almost like chicken stomachs—very heavily muscularized on the outside with a tough cornified lining, and they have a tendency to ingest gravel. This gradually disappears in spring. The same is true for some passerine birds. Redwinged blackbirds, for instance, when on the breeding grounds eat insects almost entirely. Apparently the high protein diet must be necessary for their reproduction, and in the winter when they are migrating they are mostly omnivorous and eat a lot of grain, other seeds, and the like. The stomachs again reflect this dietary change. There must be profound physiological changes associated with this as well as the gross anatomical ones which are noticeable during dissections.

TEPPERMAN: This whole business of regulation of food intake in birds is to me one of the most fascinating aspects of the whole problem of food intake regulation. At a conference in Michigan last October, Odum reported on premigratory hyperphagia in birds (Odum, 1960). In the period just before migration, and this is presumed to be related to a light stimulus—the lengthening of the day—these animals practically develop what you might call physiological hypothalamic lesions. They eat enormous quantities of food and lay down a huge amount of fat in a special migratory organ—the fat depot in the abdomen. An interesting thing about this phenomenon is that these animals are picked up on their migratory route when they hit a television tower down on the Gulf coast. The tower cuts across a number of migratory routes. Some of the animals are flying down to Central America, and some of them are going all the way down to Brazil. There, animals are carefully picked up and then put in the freezer. They are analyzed and typed, and their species is determined. By knowing the energy cost of flight of the bird and by analyzing its carcass for fat, you can tell what its migratory route is. That is, a bird that is flying 1,500 miles has 1,500 miles of fat in his depot, or a bird going only 500 miles has only 500 miles of fat in its depot organ. This apparently is very precisely regulated.

DILGER: Some years ago a colleague and I were collecting birds in the Ithaca area during spring. The day before we did this, Tennessee Warblers had not yet come in, but the day we were out they were all over. Apparently they had come in during the night and were everywhere. We shot about thirty of them; we needed skeletons and skins, and so forth. They were extremely lean; there was no noticeable fat on them at all. They weighed about nine grams each, as I recall. We decided after we went through all these birds that we needed some more. That was about four days later. We went out and shot another lot of about the same number. As it turned out, they were all gone the day following our final collection. They were here and filling up their fat reserve for the "x" miles somewhere north of us and had increased their weight from about nine grams when we first picked them up to about fifteen grams before they left four days later. Presumably, they had lost it during the flight to Ithaca, because they were lean when we saw them and four days later the fat was everywhere, not only on the belly but in the furcular crotch and on the back, all through the viscera, and it was just packed in every little niche the animal could spare—just covered with fat. This obviously may be deposited quickly and comes off very, very quickly.

TEPPERMAN: Was this light induced too?

DILGER: The initial migration is apparently light induced, but I cannot imagine that the running out of fuel, building it up again, and then going on is light induced. It must be something that is going on while the bird is on the way somewhere. As soon as it gets there, it drops to a normal weight and stays that way while breeding, starting again in the fall. I do not know if anything is known about this mechanism or not— this short-term enormous gain and loss.

HALE: I might say that I for one have been tremendously impressed by these examples of metabolic adaptation which must in many ways then work back toward the problems of those of us working in behavior or taste areas or areas of neural function.

KITCHELL: We were discussing the influence of deficiencies on the adaptation of the sensory mechanism from a neural standpoint. There is ample evidence that this can occur along the afferent pathway at many different places in the peripheral receptor mechanisms. These are called corticofugal influences, and they can occur in the cerebrum itself or in the thalamus or at the medullary level. I think this is an important place to look for these kinds of influences such as the deficiencies we are creating, and I would not, as Frommer pointed out, be at all hopeful that we could find any difference in the afferent input from the periphery in these deficient animals. I would also like to suggest that perhaps what is occurring in a deficient animal is that we are pushing the animal's preference closer to the ability of the animal to discriminate and that the stress phenomenon of the deficiency could be compared to a psychological stress such as an electrical shock if he fails to discriminate between two substances. It might be a very fruitful investigation for someone to see if a deficient animal can discriminate more acutely than an animal which is trained under an emotional stress.

FROMMER: An observation was made at Brown recently on the gustatory afferent activity recorded in the medulla in rats dosed with insulin to produce hypoglycemia. These rats showed a marked shift in preference curves, but Aldrich and Pfaffmann could not detect any change in the neural activity.

HALPERN: This was a continuation of the investigation by Pfaffmann and Hagstrom (1955) on possible changes in the chorda tympani response following insulin injection. They found none.

MORRISON: In a one-animal experiment which we were never able to repeat, Pfaffmann and I recorded from the ventromedial nucleus of the hypothalamus while injecting glucagon intravenously. We got a burst of activity which was repeatable in this one animal shortly following the glucagon injection. Nothing happened when dextrose was injected intravenously. Nothing with Ringer's solution. I was willing to swear by the results with that animal, but we tried about six more and never got it again.

TEPPERMAN: Apropos of this, I think you might be interested to know that B. K. Anand, at the Michigan meeting, reported placing recording electrodes in the ventromedial nucleus of the hypothalamus, and he claimed to get a change in activation pattern when he infused glucose into an animal (Anand, 1960). Now, this is the first evidence of this sort that I have ever heard, and I do not know of anybody other than Anand who has done this. If it holds up, it would be of extremely great interest to all of us.

Apropos of something else in the sensory versus the central change notion, Richter's adrenalectomized animal showed not only an elevated rejection threshold but also a lower selection threshold (Richter, 1936). They would accept higher concentrations than the normal rats, which seems to me you cannot have it both ways. You cannot account for both of these in terms of receptor threshold.

HALPERN: Bare (1949) reported similar data. This holds only in a two-bottle situation. Edmonds (1960a) has recently shown that in a one-bottle situation, when you get up to 2 per cent (0.34M) sodium chloride, the adrenalectomized rats either start rejecting it or die of it. They apparently cannot handle the high concentration of sodium chloride (Edmonds, 1960b). The normal rats will take quite a bit more than the adrenalectomized rats in this one-bottle test.

GOLDSTEIN: Are the terms preference and discrimination tied up with particular interpretations of where the events happened?

FROMMER: If you want to talk about taste, I would like to see the experiment involve very short-term exposures to the stimulus. If you want to talk about preference, then you can do it either way.

GOLDSTEIN: Is not there fairly general agreement among psychologists as to a clear difference in the meaning of these two terms because they both derive from a typical experiment? A discrimination experiment involves two or more stimuli of which one is usually followed by a reinforcing stimulus, defined as a change that the animal either works for or works to avoid. The preference situation, drawn from Richter, Young, and others, does not present reinforcing stimuli as a significant part of the experiment.

JACOBS: The Miller, Bailey, and Stevenson study (1950) on hypothalamic hyperphagia used several standard psychological tests which showed that, although hypothalamic obese animals ate a lot, they did not work hard for it. They suggested that these animals are not hungry. As a physiologist you may or may not be concerned at all that the animal worked hard. This may be important in discussing some situations.

GOLDSTEIN: I would agree to this. I think that the ground rules set up in that experiment were clear. They were making a distinction for the dynamic phase in hyperphagic animals, when the animals will eat anything, between being unable to stop eating and being highly motivated to eat. The tests were there to measure motivation, which did not turn out to be high, even though the animals ate a lot. So that in agreeing with your basic contention, I think that perhaps this experiment was of limited value in making the point.

CHAPTER 6

Research on Taste in the Soviet Union[*]

Herbert L. Pick, Jr.

Rᴇꜱᴇᴀʀᴄʜ ᴏɴ ᴛᴀꜱᴛᴇ in the Soviet Union, as in the United States and other Western countries, is done both by physiologists and psychologists, as well as other people interested in feeding behavior. Also similar to the United States is the fact that taste research is a rather small fraction of the total research in perception. Bronshtein, in his review of the literature on taste and odor, cites 218 Russian sources. Somewhat less than half of these are more or less directly concerned with taste. This book is probably the richest source of material on taste research in the Soviet Union. In addition, there have been several theses (for the degree of candidate of science) done on taste perception in animals since 1950. Further, the laboratory of interoception of the Pavlovian Institute in Leningrad under the direction of E. S. Airapetyants is currently engaged in the study of gustatory sensitivity. The present report is based on a visit to the Pavlovian Institute, selected library research in the Lenin Library in Moscow, and Bronshtein's review of the taste literature mentioned above. This work was in the main done while the author was a participant in the Soviet-American graduate exchange program during the academic year 1959–60.

In many cases, articles in Soviet journals seem to be incomplete when one thinks in terms of replicating experiments. Our detailed reporting of procedure and apparatus is absent, and in some cases reporting of results themselves is sketchy. This, combined with almost no use of statistical measures of reliability, often makes interpretation difficult. On the other hand, visits to laboratories usually convince one of the soundness of the experiments in conception, design, and execution.

Soviet scientists have contributed no startling new facts to the study of taste, but they have introduced methods and investigated certain variables that have been relatively neglected by us. The extensive use of the unconditioned- and conditioned-response techniques is a case in point. The unconditioned-response technique involves stimulation of the

[*] Paper submitted subsequent to the conference.

117

tongue of the subject (animal or man) with a sapid substance and recording the unconditioned saliva flow resulting from this stimulation. Other unconditioned responses can be recorded. Bronshtein (1950) reports the use of psychogalvanic responses (PGR), electroencephalograms (EEG), and vascular changes as indicators of taste stimuli. He cites one investigator who found rather fine specificity of vascular response to a taste stimulus: A sweet substance evoked dilation of vessels; a bitter substance, a slight constriction for a time, then back to normal. A salty substance evoked constriction for a short time, then dilation, etc. These "typical" responses developed after a number of applications of the stimulus. The first vascular responses to any new substance were vascular constrictions.

Saliva flow has been used to study discrimination thresholds. Bronshtein's review includes a report indicating that the nature of saliva flow varies as a function of the stimulus substance. Hydrochloric acid yields an increase in secretion of saliva which is proportional to the concentration; sodium chloride acts similarly, but not so clearly. Several investigators have studied sensitivity and change of sensitivity in dogs using such a method. Zubkova (1959) has employed this method to measure change of sensitivity in dogs under artificially induced gastritis. She introduced the stimulus through an opening made surgically in the bottom of the jaw. Using rate of saliva flow and latency as indicators, the results pointed to a heightened sensitivity to citric acid but not to sucrose, sodium chloride, and quinine hydrochloride. A recent elaboration of this method by Vasilyev (1957, 1959) gives precise control of locus of stimulation and temperature of stimulus. Saliva is collected through a small tube under vacuum. Stimulation can be applied and saliva collected independently from the two sides of the tongue and mouth (a series of experiments by Biriûkov suggests that reflex salivary secretions may be independent of gustatory afferent input [Biriûkov, 1938, and earlier papers, cited in: ONR Report ACR-48]).

The conditioned-response technique simply involves pairing a taste stimulus (relatively neutral) with an unconditioned stimulus, such as electric shock to the foreleg. Soon the taste stimulus alone will evoke leg flexion. This has been done by Andreev (1954) with cows. He conditioned discriminations between water and sodium chloride, hydrochloric acid, quinine hydrochloride, and sucrose. Discrimination thresholds were, respectively: 0.002M (0.012 per cent), 0.001M (0.037 per cent), 0.00001M (0.0036 per cent), and 0.30M (10.4 per cent). These values, except for hydrochloric acid, can be compared with preference thresholds obtained by investigators working with calves in the United States and in England. Bell and Williams (1959) reported values for sodium chloride and quinine hydrochloride of 0.105M (0.55 per cent) and 0.000024M (0.0087 per cent). Pick and Kare (1959) reported

0.022M (0.75 per cent) for sucrose. In the case of sodium chloride and quinine hydrochloride, the values obtained by Andreev are somewhat less than those obtained by the preference method. This is as it should be, since discrimination, which is presumably being measured by the conditioned-reflex method, must be at least as sensitive as preference and probably is more sensitive. The large discrepancy in the other direction between the thresholds obtained for sucrose is surprising. If this is not an artifact of the comparison, such as a different breed of animal, then it points to a large age difference in sensitivity, since Andreev's work was done on cows.

Zubkova, whose work with dogs was cited above, has mentioned (pers. comm.) that she was able to condition a dog to make a taste discrimination, but only with a great deal of difficulty. This, of course, suggests that the feasibility of this method depends to a certain extent on the animals involved.

This technique has been used to study taste sensitivity in infants. Nemanova (1941) was able to condition taste discriminations in infants just over a month in age. She used a conditioned eyelid response with a puff of air being the unconditioned stimulus. The test solution was introduced through a nipple held in the baby's mouth by an arrangement of straps. Thresholds were determined for sodium chloride, lemon juice, and sucrose. It was impossible to establish conditioned discrimination for quinine as the unconditioned response to this substance was too great itself. Thresholds for sodium chloride were obtained as low as 0.4 per cent (0.07M), for lemon juice as low as twenty drops in 100 ml. of water, and for sucrose between one per cent (0.03M) and 2.5 per cent (0.075M). (Per cent concentration refers to the number of grams of solute per hundred ml. of solution.) Also, the children were trained to differentiate these various substances from each other. Apparently, even at this early age, four taste qualities exist.

One other methodological variation used in the Soviet Union is worthy of note. Roshupkina (1954), in her experiments with dogs, used a variation of a method sometimes referred to in our literature as the one-bottle method (Benjamin, 1955). Ordinarily, this method follows the procedure of offering the test and standard taste solutions on alternate days and measuring the amounts of each consumed. Differences in these values serve as indicators of preference difference. Roshupkina drew off the consumed fluids by means of a fistula, and hence the animal could be presented with a sequence of taste solutions in a relatively short time. Preference was indicated as usual by differences in consumption. Control experiments indicated that the amount of water consumed remained stable enough from trial to trial to use as a basis of comparison. The experimental session usually lasted five hours. During this time six solutions were offered the animal. The sessions ordinarily consisted of four trials of water and two of test solutions. Preference thresholds were obtained for sodium chloride, hydrochloric acid, and quinine hydrochloride. These were 0.25 per cent (0.04M), 0.004 per cent (0.001M), and 0.0005 per cent (0.000014M), respectively. These were all rejection thresholds; that is, less test solution was consumed than water. Sucrose solutions at 5 per cent (0.15M) and 10 per cent (0.3M) were preferred to water, and the preference increased with concentration, but no thresholds were determined.

Soviet investigators, of course, have used the more traditional methods of investigating taste such as are used in standard taste-psychophysic experiments with humans, in which either sapid substances are applied to the tongue of the subject or larger amounts of the substance are tasted. The indexes with this method are the verbal reports of the subjects. The Soviet scientists have also used electrical stimulation of the tongue, again with verbal report as an index of taste.

It is interesting to note that only one electrophysiological study is cited by Bronshtein as having been carried out in the Soviet Union. This is a study by Sakhiulina (1945). However, the work of Pfaffmann (1939) and Zotterman (1935) is known; it is cited by Bronshtein (1950). Further, the simultaneous choice techniques, which are so common in the United States and England, have not been used in the Soviet Union. Mentioning the use of the preference method to one investigator, the author was told that they believe in "objective" methods in the Soviet Union and the preference method was subjective. If this is a general attitude of Soviet investigators, they obviously do not understand "objective" in the same way we do. There is some reason to believe that this is indeed the case. In the first place, in Soviet articles there is a close connection between the references to Pavlov and to his "objective" methods of investigating the mind. Implicitly, if not explicitly, one often gets the impression that the only objective methods for studying psychological processes are those devised by Pavlov. In the second place, in our science objectivity is tied up more or less with operationalism. The Soviets attempt to avoid this philosophical basis with their dialectical materialism.

Physiology in the Soviet Union covers a somewhat different range of topics than it does in the United States. There is much overlap, of course, but in particular the largest amount of work that we call comparative or physiological psychology is done there by physiologists. In connection with taste work, this leads to a classical physiological approach including anatomical and histological studies, on the one hand, and to a Pavlovian conditional-reflex physiology, on the other.

In connection with what above is termed a classical physiological approach, the Soviet investigators have pursued some of the same lines that have been investigated in the West. I will mention two examples.

One is a study of a large number of neurosurgical cases by Ageeva-Maikova (1946). This investigator, on the basis of studies of loss of taste sensitivity which coincided with pathology of the Vth, VIIth, or IXth cranial nerves, convinced herself that the only nerves directly involved in the mediation of taste are the glossopharyngeal and the chorda tympani. Details of the results are sketchy. The other example is the work of Roshupkina (1954) mentioned earlier in connection with the one-bottle method. She examined the effect of dissection of various nerves associated with taste on the taste sensitivity of dogs. In general, thresholds were raised for sodium chloride, quinine hydrochloride, and sometimes for sucrose, but not for hydrochloric acid. However, there were large individual differences in the effect. The operation was done in two successive stages, leaving decreasing amounts of sensory innervation.

In connection with the Pavlovian physiological approach, consideration has been given to the similarity and differences between the taste analyzer and the other analyzers, as well as the interaction between analyzers. An analyzer refers to a receptor system including the peripheral and central, the afferent and efferent, aspects. Thus the visual analyzer includes the eye, optic nerve, the various intermediate nuclei, the visual cortex, and the efferent fibers controlling eye movements, pupillary adjustment, etc.

Abuladze (1952) notes that, if one side of the tongue is stimulated with a saliva-evoking substance, saliva is produced on that side of the mouth only, unless the stimulus is very strong (in which case the other side produces a lesser amount of saliva) or unless the glands on the other side of the mouth had been producing saliva during a relatively short preceding period (approximately five to ten minutes). Abuladze was interested in the general question of the one-sided effect of this stimulation and its relation to a conditioned response. In particular, if a two-sided stimulus—for example, sound to both ears or stimulation of corresponding points of the skin on opposite sides of the body—is conditioned to evoke a one-sided salivatory response, will the stimulation of either side by itself evoke the salivatory response? Because of the difficulty in completely isolating one ear from sound while stimulating the other, this experiment was done with tactual stimulation only. Dogs were conditioned with stimulation to both sides of the body as a conditioned stimulus and a saliva-evoking substance to just one side of the tongue as the unconditioned stimulus. Testing for response to each side of the body stimulated independently, stimulation of the body on the same side as the unconditioned response was much more effective in evoking saliva than contralateral stimulation. This is interpreted as supporting some sort of lateral specificity in conditioned linking of the taste analyzer with other analyzing systems. The data supported this

conclusion but were reported so sparsely (and, as usual, without indication of reliability) that the experiment should be replicated.

Another approach to the study of the analyzers is called intersensory
facilitation and inhibition. Dobriakova (1939), working with humans,
has studied the changes of electrical sensitivity of vision and taste under the influence of optical and taste stimuli. Stimulation by bright
illumination (1,500 lux) after adaptation to 2 lux increased electrical
sensitivity of both the tongue and the eye. Dark adaptation decreased
electrical sensitivity of both organs. Stimulation of the tongue by
various chemicals generally tended to decrease sensitivity of both
organs. Thus, the sensitivity of both analyzers seems to operate in
parallel, but the effect of stimulation of the two receptors is apparently
in opposite directions. Torniva (1940) measured change of sensitivity
to sodium chloride under three conditions of light: no light, a "normal"
condition, and 350 lux. In general, sensitivity increased with the
amount of light, but individual differences were large, and again reliability of results could be questioned.

In comparing the taste analyzer with other receptor systems,
Bronshtein (1950) reviewed the literature on taste adaptation—after
images, contrast, and taste mixtures. In all of this, he relies heavily on
such foreign investigators as Allen and Weinberg, Bujas, and von Skram-
lik, although there has been some Soviet work on these topics. He reports
that A. A. Bronshtein (1947) obtained aftertastes from electrical stimulation of the tongue by direct current, if this current was applied in a
particular rhythm. These were usually but not always accompanied by
tactual sensations. Another phenomenon described by Bronshtein he
calls sensitization. This refers to an increase of sensitivity, with repeated threshold determinations made every two or three minutes during the course of an hour. The sensitivity to quinine under such conditions usually increased from 30 to 110 per cent, and this was usually
accompanied by an increase in sensitivity to a sweet substance (sucrose). However, cross-sensitization was a complex affair. For example,
sensitization to salt in one subject led to a decrease in sensitivity to
sucrose.

Turning from the influence of more or less purely sensory effects on
the taste analyzer, we should mention a number of internal factors that
have been studied with respect to their effect on taste. Gusev (1940a)
has investigated the effect of hunger on taste sensitivity. He reports
changes of taste sensitivity with increasing hours of fasting. Subjects
were given ten cc. samples of the taste stimulus and asked to state if
this had a taste, and if so what sort of taste. They then rinsed out their
mouths with distilled water and were once again asked to compare the
previous solution with the distilled water. Subjects were tested in the
case of sucrose three times a day: one and a half, four, and eight hours

after eating, and in the case of sodium chloride, hydrochloric acid, and quinine sulphate, one and a half and four hours after eating. Results are interpreted as showing increasing sensitivity to sucrose (seven subjects) and to sodium chloride (four subjects) with increasing hunger. Results in these two cases probably would not reach statistical significance by our criteria, and in the case of hydrochloric acid and quinine sulphate they were even more questionable. The subjects were tested on several successive days, and the conclusions were based on the number of days when sensitivity changed in relation to time of fasting. These results are at odds with those of Meyer (1952), who found with a larger number of subjects no change of taste sensitivity as hunger increased from zero to 34 hours. However, Meyer made only one series of determinations on each subject.

An interesting sidelight on Gusev's results is the question he raises as to whether the change of sensitivity is correlated with the subjective feeling of hunger or merely the objective need for food. Questioning the subjects as to their feelings of hunger, he found no correlation between experienced hunger and change of sensitivity and hence concludes in favor of objective need.

From Bronshtein (1950) one learns that Soviet investigators have found that oxygen deficiency tends to decrease sensitivity to sugar, while at first increasing but then decreasing sensitivity to substances representing the other taste qualities. Also, he reports studies of the effect of various diseases, such as tuberculosis, epilepsy, palsy, and diabetes on taste sensitivity. Results in the case of tuberculosis suggest that when the disease is in both respiratory tract and lungs the decrement of taste sensitivity is greatest; when in the lungs alone, somewhat less. Bone tuberculosis seems to have no appreciable effect on taste sensitivity.

Let us look next at a few rather interesting external factors whose effect on taste sensitivity the Soviets have investigated. The effect of high external temperature on taste sensitivity of dogs has been investigated by Krol'-Livshits (1933). She used saliva production of the parotid gland as the index of perceived taste, introducing the test solution through a surgically made opening in the cheek. Chemicals tested were sodium chloride, hydrochloric acid, and quinine. An interesting side result was that the threshold for sucrose, using this method, was 1.5M (51.3 per cent) to 2.0M (68.5 per cent). The concentration was so high that sucrose was not used for this experiment. A dog was tested under normal conditions, then put in a chamber at a temperature of 50° C. and a relative humidity of 35 per cent for approximately an hour. After this session the dog was allowed 15 minutes at normal temperature and his threshold again determined. With the heat treatment every second or third day, thresholds increased to some degree, but, under the greater stress of daily heat treatments, they went up still further for sodium chloride and hydrochloric acid. Typical values are shown in Table 1. Under alternate-day heat treatments, thresholds returned to normal by the next day. However, after a series of daily treatments, the thresholds remained high for a longer period, returning to normal only after several days without heat treatment.

Bronshtein reports another study carried out by Timofeev and Krol'-Livshits (1933) on taste sensitivity in workers of various occupations. The individuals studied included cooks and typographers among others. Taste sensitivity of cooks in general increased with time on the job, while that of typographers decreased with respect to bitter, salty, and, to a lesser extent, sour substances. Another investigator, Ufland (1928), reported that lead workers showed increased sensitivity to

TABLE 1

CHANGE OF TASTE THRESHOLD AFTER EXPOSURE
TO HIGH EXTERNAL TEMPERATURE

(Data from Krol'-Livshits, 1933)

Taste Substance	Initial Threshold	Threshold after Heat Treatment Every Second or Third Day	Threshold after Daily Treatment
NaCl.........	2.32 per cent (0.4M)	2.75 per cent (0.47M)	3.70 per cent (0.63M)
HCl..........	0.006 per cent (0.0016M)	0.009 per cent (0.0025M)	0.012 per cent (0.0033M)
Quinine........ Hydrochloride..	0.016 per cent (0.00044M)	0.024 per cent (0.00067M)	0.024 per cent (0.00067M)

sweet substances. The report of these studies by Bronshtein do not indicate whether they were longitudinal over a period of time on the job or whether cross-sectional of all the workers on a job at a particular time.

Soviet researchers have directly manipulated the stimulus itself in some cases. Here the variable given most attention has been temperature. Bronshtein indicates that Schreiber (1887) had found that there was an optimum temperature range for sensitivity of taste substances representative of four taste qualities. This range was about that of body temperature, and sensitivity decreased if the temperature was changed very much from this range. The change of sensitivity was quite marked in the case of quinine and an acid but less so in the case of a salt and a sugar. Pfaffmann (1959b) reviews much evidence on the relation between temperature and sensitivity. Much of it tends to confirm a curvilinear relation between the two variables, but increasing temperature does not consistently increase sensitivity. Unfortunately, as Pfaffmann points out, the best controlled work, that of Hahn and Günther (1932), did not cover a wide range of temperature.

In the Soviet Union there have been at least two studies showing the effect of temperature on taste in animals. Krol'-Livshits (1935), using an unconditioned saliva response of dogs as an index, found that the threshold of sodium chloride had a low level at an intermediate temperature range, i.e., there was an optimum temperature range for sensitivity to sodium chloride. This range was 38–42° C. for one dog, the threshold increasing sharply above and below this. The change for hydrochloric acid was rather small, and its reliability difficult to interpret. Distilled water evoked no salivatory response except at the top of the range studied (48–50° C.). Another study is part of Roshupkina's thesis (1954), referred to previously. In this investigation the amount consumed in a modified one-bottle procedure was the index. Consumption of water increased as the temperature of the water was raised from five to 20 to 30° C. It is unfortunate that the temperature range was not extended to the range of 48–50° C. used in Krol'-Livshits' study. The effect of temperature change on consumption of sodium chloride, hydrochloric acid, and quinine hydrochloride solutions was also studied. In the case of sodium chloride and hydrochloric acid solutions, increasing temperature decreases consumption at a constant concentration, but with quinine hydrochloride the opposite effect occurs. This could be interpreted as increasing sensitivity to hydrochloric acid and sodium chloride and decreasing sensitivity to the quinine hydrochloride with increase of temperature over the range covered. With such an interpretation, it falls into line with the results obtained with humans by Hahn and Günther, mentioned earlier.

Finally, as far as taste classification is concerned, the Soviet research in general follows the classical approach. For example, Bronshtein even reproduces Henning's taste tetrahedron, although he has some reservations about the value of it. It might be mentioned in connection with taste classification that, according to Bronshtein, Lomonosov made a seven-taste classification in 1752. This is a rather early classification. Boring (1942) cites only three that are earlier, one in 1592 and the other two in 1751.

Gusev (1940*b*) reports an interesting study of the intellectual mediation of taste sensations. It actually is a follow-up study to the one described above on the effect of hunger on taste sensitivity. In the present paper Gusev analyzed the errors made in taste judgments in the previous study, in which the subjects' task was to make an absolute judgment of the taste of a ten ml. sample of the substance. On many of the trials the subjects classified the taste solution incorrectly. Table 2 indicates which substances were classified incorrectly and into which categories they were placed. Table 2 refers to those judgments made one to one and a half hours after eating. Those made four hours after eating present a similar picture. It would seem that various confusions occur in classifying threshold concentrations of taste stimuli, and these are not reciprocal in nature. Sweet and bitter are mutually confused, but sour is confused with salty mostly, and salty with sweet. This sort of phenomenon was reported as long ago as 1919 by Rengvist, who is cited to this effect by Pfaffmann (1959*b*).

Gusev goes on to consider the nature of these confusions by analysis of verbal reports of the subjects, and he comes to the conclusion that expectation of the subject plays an important role in classification at these threshold values. Also, he considers that incorrect classifications can be divided into two categories: those in which the present taste is compared to some sort of mental standard of what a threshold concentration of a particular substance should be, and those in which the taste is immediately perceived by the sense quality to which it gives rise. Presumably, the first sort of errors can be corrected by training to some extent.

TABLE 2

INCORRECT CLASSIFICATIONS OF TASTE STIMULI

(Data from Gusev, 1940*b*)

TASTE STIMULUS	PERCENTAGE OF CASES CLASSIFIED AS:				TOTAL INCORRECT
	Salty	Sour	Bitter	Sweet	
Sweet...........	14.5	19.5	42.0	....	76.0
Salty...........	....	6.0	8.0	67.0	81.0
Sour...........	43.0	....	19.0	21.0	83.0
Bitter...........	3.0	0.0	....	24.0	27.0

There have been a few studies by Soviet scientists attempting to find a psychochemical structure for taste. In general these have had the same discouraging results as those appearing in our literature. In fact, Bronshtein (1950), in his review, pretty much follows Moncrieff (1946).

Thus, in summing up, one would say that Soviet contributions to the study of taste have been rather of a methodological than a substantive nature, particularly the unconditioned- and conditioned-reflex methods as well as the modification of the one-bottle method. In addition, imaginative work has been started on such variables as oxygen deficiency, external temperature, and occupational setting. Philosophically, perhaps the differential in emphasis on taste research between the Soviet Union and the United States reflects a natural difference in interest between one country which has spent a good deal of time during the last forty years on starvation rations and another country which has spent a good deal of time dieting to avoid the bad effects of overeating.

CHAPTER 7

Summaries

Martin W. Schein

This conference started with a discussion of the phylogeny of taste by Kare. He raised two questions at the outset: First, what is the survival value of taste preferences; and, second, is there any significance to the absolute number of taste buds present in an animal? The first question is not to be confused with the survival value of simple chemical reception but rather is directed at the hedonic function of taste preferences.

Anatomically, the lowest common denominator in taste work is that structure called the taste bud. Such receptors are similar in appearance in both mammals and birds, yet the responses of various species, indeed often of various individuals within a species, to a specific chemical agent may vary from complete rejection to a high degree of selection. For example, in the discussion and presentation it was pointed out that strain differences exist in rats' neural responses to sugars, and it was further suggested that saccharin preferences in pigs may be heritable. Again, the range of preferences for specific sugars varies from acceptance through rejection within groups of calves. Thus, there are few if any generalizations that we can safely make regarding the phylogeny of taste preferences, even if we limit the discussion solely to mammals and birds.

In an effort to determine what physical or chemical properties might be associated with taste preferences, Kare tested osmotic pressure, viscosity, optical rotation, reducing ability, melting point, molecular configuration, solubility, nutritive value, toxicity, and even the "sweetness" as judged by humans. None of these properties was even closely related to selection or rejection of a compound by chickens. Thus, discrimination seems to be based on an absolute specificity even to the level of the stereoisomer.

To extend the significance of the absolute number of taste receptors to a species, Kare suggested a search for auxiliary internal receptors which might influence the acceptance or rejection of a substance. For example, the chicken on an adequate diet is almost indifferent to glucose and sucrose, even at fairly high concentrations, but markedly rejects xylose. When ingested, glucose is removed from the ligated crop while xylose is not. Yet no receptors have been found in any part of the buccal cavity other than the dozen or so taste buds already described. At the present state of our knowledge, the only generalization that can safely be made is that the taste preferences of each species must be considered independently. Indeed, in view of the large variation even within a species, one must be careful to use an adequate sample size to overcome individual differences. Furthermore, since there are indications that preferences may vary with respect to physiological age, even this factor must be considered in subsequent work.

The question of the relationship between taste preferences and total intake was also discussed. Kare pointed out that intake can be reduced by adding increasing amounts of an unacceptable compound; the more that is added, the lower the intake. Therefore, the converse should theoretically hold: it should be possible to increase intake by reducing still further the concentration of whatever rejected substances are present.

Turning the question the other way around, Jacobs considered the idea of intake governing taste preferences. Specifically, he explored the concept of an osmotic pressure, postingestion factor which has been proposed as a mechanism governing glucose intake. First, he traced the history of the major research which implicated osmotic pressure as a postingestion factor and then showed that osmotic pressure could not possibly be the sole or even the major factor involved.

Long-term preference testing (several hours of exposure to a choice situation) typically yields an inverted-U-shaped curve depicting the relationship between the concentration of an acceptable substance and the quantity of its intake. Thus, a specific concentration is associated with maximum intake; deviations from this concentration result in reduced intake. In a short-term preference test (less than an hour of exposure), the relationship between concentration and intake is essentially linear: the higher the concentration of a preferred substance, the higher the intake. Presumably, the intake is governed in a short-term exposure by peripheral receptor stimulation (taste), but in long-term exposures postingestional factors come into play.

On the basis of investigations by Shuford and by McCleary, osmotic pressure in the animal's stomach was implicated as the most important postingestion factor governing intake. Thus, rats with a hypertonic glucose stomach load should drink more water than those with isotonic or hypotonic loads. Similarly, in a two-choice situation in which water and varying concentrations of glucose are offered, rats with a hypertonic glucose stomach load should take more water than glucose, as opposed to those with isotonic or hypotonic loads. However, Jacobs found that the increased water intake was not demonstrable with rats that were not previously water-deprived. Higher concentrations of glucose, administered by stomach loading, increased water intake only when paired with water-deprived animals, whether they had hypertonic glucose stomach loads or not.

Therefore, Jacobs suggested that water intake is governed primarily by deprivation dehydration; likewise, glucose intake is governed by the amount of food ingested and not by its osmotic properties. He also pointed out that the caloric values of ingested foods roughly fit McCleary's, Shuford's, and his own data, and therefore might be considered as an adequate alternative to osmotic pressure as a postingestion factor.

Irving Y. Fishman

I would like to summarize briefly some of the types of peripheral responses that have been obtained. In single fibers the responses are arhythmic, with the amplitude characteristic of the individual fiber. We must look to frequency and temporal pattern to obtain variation in a given fiber. In almost all instances of stimulation of the peripheral receptor with monovalent salts, acids, and quinine, the responses start with a rapid initial burst of impulses which quickly decay in number to a more or less steady frequency. During the steady state there may be large, brief, temporal variations, although the over-all frequency to a given stimulant is constant and reproducible if averaged over several seconds of stimulation. The steady state activity of salt stimulation shows little tendency to fatigue on constant stimulation for three minutes or longer. The frequency of the initial burst, however, is somewhat more variable than the steady state level of activity and is, I believe, less reproducible.

The greatest departure from this type of response pattern in single fibers comes with a gradual build-up to a steady state without the sharp initial response and is followed by a gradual decrease in steady state activity to a low level of response. This is exhibited most frequently by divalents such as calcium and magnesium and with citrate anion.

Only in a few instances have I observed the steady state response to be rhythmic, and this only with sucrose stimulation. In these instances the activity was burstlike with impulses grouped together and a fairly constant interval between groups. Beidler has also reported seeing such rhythmic activity. Integrated responses are notably similar to the individual, unintegrated, single-fiber responses.

Kitchell brought up some points that should be mentioned again concerning the limitations of the integrator technique. I am personally quite confident of the validity of data so obtained, providing proper attention is given to the limitations. One must remember what is being recorded and must use caution in interpreting the data. With the proper precautions the integrator (summator) is a perfectly good tool, and certainly the reproducibility (within fairly narrow limits of tolerance) that one is able to demonstrate in different subjects of the same species indicates that the results are reasonably valid. In addition, the degree with which the responses of a random population of single-fiber responses can be correlated with integrator data for the same species—as I have demonstrated using my own single-fiber data and those previously obtained by Pfaffmann in the rat, cat, and rabbit—reinforces this conclusion. The integrator is not really an integrator, as defined by the physicist, but rather a summator, and perhaps this is the term which should be applied. It is, basically, a half-wave rectifier which summates the area under the curves of the impulses.

Another point which should be made with regard to using the integrator is that there are definite limitations in comparing experiments with different animals. That is, it is difficult to compare a hamster experiment with a rat experiment because of the variable conditions involved. As Kitchell has mentioned, the position and size of the electrodes, the condition of the subject animal, the dissection, and the time-constant of the integrator are all variable. However, it is quite possible, and easy, to compare responses during any given experiment, providing one uses a suitable reference stimulant. This is usually accomplished by selecting the inorganic salt which elicits the greatest response in the species of animal under study and using this salt as a control throughout the course of the experiment. As long as the response to a specific concentration of the control remains constant, the responses to other test solutions are comparable and the responses relative to the control-substance responses are reproducible from animal to animal of the same species.

Kitchell has also pointed out that the integrator is a rectifier with resistance-capacitance couplings, so that changing the time-constant is merely a matter of changing the ratio of the condenser to the resistors in the coupling. The time-constant can be selected to suit the investigator. The time-constant to which he refers is the time lag of the recording galvanometer that is being used to graph the time course of the response. The characteristics of the initial rapid response can, therefore, be considerably altered by the simple act of changing the time-constant. As Kitchell has suggested, those who use the integrator should develop the habit of stating exactly what the time-constant of the experiment was or, at least, of expressing the fact that it was not changed during the course of the experiment and of stating whether it was a long or a short time-constant. I could not agree more. It should be noted, however, that, since the time-constant does not affect the magnitude of the steady state response, the integrator is a good steady state analyzer. I think we need not worry about the time-constant in considering the steady state data. This is one reason, beside the greater variability of the initial response, why I prefer to analyze a record by using the steady state response magnitude in lieu of the initial response.

Frommer's and Benjamin's presentations regarding thalamic gustatory activities from the medial extension of the ventral nucleus impressed me particularly in one regard. It is very interesting that the integrated record of the asynchronous discharges obtained were surprisingly like the integrated record obtained from the peripheral response. One thing which should be noted is the shape of the concentration curves obtained with sodium and potassium chlorides in the thalamus. In both instances the curves have the same shape as those elicited in the peripheral nerve by the same salt.

Let me mention one additional matter of which we are all aware. The gross sensory experience in any given instance includes not only chemosensory information from the peripheral receptors but tactile and thermal information as well. It comes not merely from a localized area of the tongue but from a wide receptor field, which makes possible complex spatial and temporal patterns of stimulation, reinforced and modified by tongue movements and saliva. The body of information which reaches the central nervous system is, then, large, complex, and variable.

Trygg Engen

As Pilgrim pointed out, the session in which he and Christensen presented papers was probably the most molar behavioral section of the conference. I think we tended to talk about more general problems in that context. Pilgrim's work was concerned with human taste behavior— one might call it that—or the use of subjective rating scales in dealing with interactions between four familiar agents: caffeine, sodium chloride, sucrose, and citric acid. Briefly, the results show evidence both of enhancement and masking effects among these four agents. A stimulating part of his talk was concerned with the judges' confusion between sour and bitter. This led to the possibility of confusion among all four qualities and their chemical counterparts. At this point the so-called "nonbehaviorists" became very interested in the so-called "behavioral" problem. MacLeod questioned the meaning and usefulness of the concept of "sense." My prediction about this would be that the neurophysiologists and psychologists will have much discussion about this problem in the future. What is exciting about it, I believe, is that here we might come closer to a unified taste theory, one dealing both with conscious experience (which we guess about from behavior) and mediating physiological mechanisms.

Christensen presented the interesting history of preference methodology in animal work. He concluded with a demonstration of the up-and-down method applied to the electronic preference tester. The data Christensen presented on concentrations of equally acceptable chemicals for the rat indicated a way to a quantitative approach. We speak often about quantification when we merely mean finding a convenient way in which to count something, and we are not usually concerned as to whether or not these procedures meaningfully quantify the variables of importance in the sense of taste. We tend to deal with the units we borrowed from chemists and physicists, and we accept them as relevant to any behavioral problem.

Edgar B. Hale

I was tremendously impressed by the numerous examples of metabolic and nutritional adaptations presented by Tepperman and Heggeness. All suggest that somewhere along the line taste should be playing a role in some manner. It is tempting to accept the possibility that all adaptive adjustments of intake may reflect a common mechanism as suggested by Harriman. However, with the large variety of adaptations noted, we should be challenged to investigate thoroughly several diverse examples in order to explore the alternate possibility that there may be many different ways in which taste contributes to the adaptive response.

Equally impressive are the examples of metabolic adaptations which start as essentially intake functions determined by taste preferences or imposed by the investigator. Recognition of the role of intake in inducing metabolic adaptations is an encouraging development. I hope that students of behavior will become equally alert to the possible variety and extent of metabolic adjustments produced in deprived animals and to the consequent effects on behavior.

In recent years our attention has been directed to glucostatic and other mechanisms as regulators of food intake. With this development we find a concomitant interest in the breakdown of the glucostatic mechanism as a factor in obesity. Now that a thalamic taste nucleus has been identified and described for us by Frommer and Benjamin, malfunctions of this nucleus as a factor regulating food intake pose interesting possibilities. I believe we may look forward with confidence to important and exciting findings in this area very soon.

The problem of regulation of food intake in a need-free animal should not be overlooked. My interest in this problem reflects in part the temper of the times. As you know, we are said to be living in an "affluent society." I wish to submit the thesis that techniques and problems investigated in the laboratory by behaviorists follow the same sequence as sociological changes in human society. In feudal society human behavior was controlled primarily by means of punishment and forced labor. I think of the threat of the whiplash held over the galley slave as an example. It perhaps was to be expected that the first extensive attempts in psychological laboratories to manipulate the behavior of animals would employ electric shock. With the advent of the industrial revolution, we find a shift from forced labor to the manipulation of human activity through extreme deprivation accompanied by reward units so small that people were compelled to work long hours to acquire enough to meet their minimum needs. Similarly, psychologists in the laboratory more recently have objected to shock as being too extreme and have sought to manipulate behavior through enlightened positive reinforcement. Skinner has advanced to this stage with his reinforcement schedules as a means of obtaining high work levels in his deprived laboratory animals. With the coming of the affluent society, traditional rewards became ineffective as there were no longer deprived individuals. Consequently, what I prefer to call "high stimulus pressure" has now come to play a major role in the manipulation of human behavior. Others might refer to it as too much advertising or too frequent change of models. As might have been predicted from my thesis, one of the major developments in behavior research during the past decade has been the great interest in curiosity, novelty, and stimulus pressure as determinants of behavior. Madison Avenue, mothers with small children, and many others are actively engaged in efforts to manipulate the food intake of need-free humans. I am confident we shall see a parallel effort in psychological laboratories.

Bibliography

ABLES, M., and R. M. BENJAMIN. 1960. Thalamic relay nucleus for taste in albino rat. Jour. Neurophysiol., **23**:376.

ABULADZE, K. C. 1952. Toward a Physiology of the Oral Chemical Taste Analyzer. Trudy 15ogo sovesh. po probl. vysshi. nervnoi deiatel 'nosti posviash. 50 letiu ucheniya akad. I. P. Pavlova ob uclovnÿkh refleksakh. Publishing House of Academy of Science, USSR, Moscow and Leningrad.

ADOLPH, E. F. 1947. Urges to eat and drink in rats. Amer. Jour. Physiol., **151**:110.

ADOLPH, E. F., J. P. BARKER, and P. A. HOY. 1954. Multiple factors in thirst. Amer. Jour. Physiol., **178**:538.

AGEEVA-MAĬKOVA, O. G. 1946. Neuro-surgical data on the path of taste conducting nerves. Voprosÿ nerokhirurgii, **10**(No. 5):661.

ANAND, B. K. 1960. Nervous regulation of food intake. Amer. Jour. Clin. Nutr., **8**:529.

ANDERSON, R. J. 1950. Taste thresholds in stimulus mixtures. Ph.D. thesis, University of Michigan.

ANDERSSON, B., S. LANDGREN, L. OLSSON, and Y. ZOTTERMAN. 1950. The sweet taste fibres of the dog. Acta Physiol. Scand., **21**:105.

ANDREEV, N. A. 1954. Toward a physiology of the taste analyzer of cattle. Unpublished candidate of science dissertation on deposit in Lenin Library, Moscow.

APPELBERG, B. 1958. Species differences in the taste qualities mediated through the glossopharyngeal nerve. Acta Physiol. Scand., **44**:129.

APPELBERG, B., and S. LANDGREN. 1958. The localization of the thalamic relay in the specific sensory path from the tongue of the cat. Acta Physiol. Scand., **42**:342.

AREY, L. 1954. Developmental Anatomy. W. B. Saunders Co., Philadelphia.

BALDWIN, B. A., F. R. BELL, and R. L. KITCHELL. 1959. Gustatory nerve impulses in ruminant ungulates. Jour. Physiol. (London), **146**:14P.

BARADI, A. F., and G. H. BOURNE. 1953. Gustatory and olfactory epithelia. Internat. Rev. Cytol., **2**:289.

BARE, J. K. 1949. The specific hunger for sodium chloride in normal and adrenalectomized white rats. Jour. Comp. Physiol. Psychol., **42**:242.

BEACH, F. A. 1956. Characteristics of masculine "sex drive." *In:* M. R. JONES (ed.), Nebraska Symposium on Motivation. Univ. Nebraska Press, Lincoln.

BEACH, F. A., and L. JORDAN. 1956. Sexual exhaustion and recovery in the male rat. Quart. Jour. Exp. Psychol., Vol. **8** (Part 3).

BEEBE-CENTER, J. G., M. S. ROGERS, W. H. ATKINSON, and D. H. O'CONNEL. 1959. Sweetness and saltiness of compound solutions of sucrose and NaCl as a function of concentration of solutes. Jour. Exp. Psychol., **57**:231.

BEIDLER, L. M. 1953. Properties of chemoreceptors of tongue of rat. Jour. Neurophysiol., **16**:595.

————. 1962. Mechanism of taste receptor stimulation. Progress in Biophysics and Biophysical Chemistry. (In press.)

BEIDLER, L. M., I. Y. FISHMAN, and C. W. HARDIMAN. 1955. Species differences in taste responses. Amer. Jour. Physiol., **181**:235.

BEIDLER, L. M., M. S. NEJAD, R. L. SMALLMAN, and H. TATEDA. 1960. Rat taste cell proliferation. Fed. Proc., **19**:302.

BELL, F. R., and H. L. WILLIAMS. 1959. Threshold values for taste in monozygotic twin calves. Nature, **183**:345.

BENJAMIN, R. M. 1955. Cortical taste mechanisms studied by two different test procedures. Jour. Comp. Physiol. Psychol., **48**:119.

BENJAMIN, R. M., and K. AKERT. 1959. Cortical and thalamic areas involved in taste discrimination in the albino rat. Jour. Comp. Neurol., **111**:231.

BENJAMIN, R. M., and R. EMMERS. 1960. Localization of separate cortical areas for taste and tactile tongue afferents in squirrel monkey (*Saimiri sciureus*). Fed. Proc., **19**:291.

BHATTACHARYA, B. K., S. B. BROACHA, and T. DE 'LIMA. 1951. The metabolic fate of invert sugar. Ind. Jour. Med. Res., **39**:377.

BLAKESLEE, A. F., and A. L. FOX. 1932. Our different taste worlds. P. T. C. as a demonstration of genetic differences in taste. Jour. Heredity, **23**:97.

BÖRNSTEIN, W. S. 1940. Cortical representation of taste in man and monkey. I. Functional and anatomical relations of taste, olfaction, and somatic sensibility. Yale Jour. Biol. Med., **12**:719.

BORING, E. G. 1942. Sensation and Perception in the History of Experimental Psychology. Appleton-Century-Crofts, Inc., New York.

————. 1950. A History of Experimental Psychology. Appleton-Century-Crofts, Inc., New York.

BREDER, C., and P. RASQUIN. 1943. Chemical sensory reactions in the Mexican blind characins. Zoologica, **28**:169.

BROBECK, J. R. 1946. Mechanism of the development of obesity in animals with hypothalamic lesions. Physiol. Rev., **26**:541.

BROBECK, J. R., J. TEPPERMAN, and C. N. H. LONG. 1943. Experimental hypothalamic hyperphagia in the albino rat. Yale Jour. Biol. Med., **15**:831.

BRONSHTEIN, A. 1947. Conditions of arousal of tactual after images under inadequate (electrical) stimulation of the skin analyzer. Trudy VMA im. S. M. Kirova, **42**:23.

―――. 1950. Taste and Odor. Publishing House of the Academy of Science, USSR, Moscow and Leningrad.

BRUSH, F. R., and S. A. AMITIN. 1960. Early experience and quinine hydrochloride preference. Abstract in Annual Program of Eastern Psychological Association Meeting, April 15 and 16, 1960, p. 32.

CARPENTER, J. A. 1956. Species differences in taste preferences. Jour. Comp. Physiol. Psychol., **49**:139.

CHAMBERS, R. M. 1956*a*. Effects of intravenous glucose injections on learning, general activity, and hunger drive. Jour. Comp. Physiol. Psychol., **49**:558.

―――. 1956*b*. Some physiological bases for reinforcing properties of reward injections. *Ibid.*, p. 565.

CHRISTENSEN, K. R. 1960. Isohedonic contours in the sucrose–sodium chloride area of gustatory stimulation. Ph.D. thesis, University of Illinois.

COHEN, M. J., S. HAGIWARA, and Y. ZOTTERMAN. 1955. The response spectrum of taste fibres in the cat: A single fibre analysis. Acta Physiol. Scand., **33**:316.

COHEN, M. J., S. LANDGREN, L. STRÖM, and Y. ZOTTERMAN. 1957. Cortical reception of touch and taste in the cat. Acta Physiol. Scand., Vol. **40**, Suppl. 135.

COHEN, T., and L. GITMAN. 1959. Oral complaints and taste perception in the aged. Jour. Geront., **14**:294.

COOPER, R. M., I. BILASH, and J. P. ZUBECK. 1959. The effect of age on taste sensitivity. Jour. Geront., **14**:56.

COPPOCK, H. W., and R. M. CHAMBERS. 1954. Reinforcement of position preference by automatic intravenous injection of glucose. Jour. Comp. Physiol. Psychol., **47**:355.

DAVIS, J. O., C. J. C. CARPENTER, C. R. AYERS, and R. C. BAHN. 1960. Increased aldosterone secretion following decapitation and subsequent bleeding of hypophysectomized dogs. Abstracted in: Abstracts, Endocrine Soc., 42d Meeting, p. 14.

DE GROOT, J. 1959. The rat forebrain in stereotaxic coordinates. Trans. Royal Neth. Acad. Sci., **52**, No. 4.

DEMBER, W. N. 1956. Response by the rat to environmental change. Jour. Comp. Physiol. Psychol., **49**:93.

DETHIER, V. G. 1956. Chemoreceptor mechanisms. *In:* R. G. GRENELL and L. MULLINS (eds.), Molecular Structure and Functional Activity of Nerve Cells. A.I.B.S. Washington.

DEUTSCH, J. A., and A. D. JONES. 1960. Diluted water: an explanation of the rat's preference for saline. Jour. Comp. Physiol. Psychol., **53**:122.

DILGER, W. C. 1960. The comparative ethology of the African parrot genus *Agapornis*. Zeit. f. Tierpsych., **17**:649.

DOBRIAKOVA, O. A. 1939. Concerning the parallel in changes of electrical sensitivity of organs of vision and taste under the influence of optical and taste stimuli. Fiziologicheskiĭ Zhurnal SSSR, **26**:192.

DUKES, H. H. 1955. The Physiology of Domestic Animals. Comstock, Ithaca, New York.

DUNCAN, C. J. 1960. Preference tests and the sense of taste in the feral pigeon. Animal Behaviour, **8**:54.

EDMONDS, C. J. 1960*a*. Fluid intake and exchangeable body sodium of normal and adrenalectomized rats given various concentrations of saline to drink. Quart. Jour. Exp. Physiol., **45**:163.

————. 1960*b*. The effect of prolonged intragastric infusions of isotonic and hypertonic saline on water and sodium excretion and on exchangeable body sodium in normal and adrenalectomized rats. *Ibid.*, p. 171.

EMMERS, R., R. M. BENJAMIN, and M. F. ABLES. 1960. Differential localization of taste and tongue tactile afferents in the rat thalamus. Fed. Proc., **19**:286.

ENGELMANN, C. 1937. Vom Geschmackssinn des Huhns. Forschungen und Fortschritte, **13**:425.

FABIAN, F. W., and H. B. BLUM. 1943. Relative taste potency of some basic food constituents and their competitive and compensatory action. Food Res., **8**:179.

FERGUSON, L. N., and A. R. LAWRENCE. 1958. The physicochemical aspects of the sense of taste. Jour. Chem. Ed., **35**:436.

FICKEN, M. S., and M. R. KARE. 1961. Individual variation in the ability to taste (Abstract). Poultry Sci. (In press.)

FISHMAN, I. Y. 1957. Single fiber gustatory impulses in rat and hamster. Jour. Cell. and Comp. Physiol., **49**:319.

FLEISHER, L. 1956. The effects of maturation on the gustatory sensitivity of guinea pigs. M.S. thesis, Brown University.

FREGLY, M. J. 1956. Effect of renal hypertension on the preference threshold of rats for sodium chloride. Amer. Jour. Physiol., **187**:288.

————. 1959. Specificity of sodium chloride aversion of hypertensive rats. *Ibid.*, **196**:1326.

FREGLY, M. J., N. B. MARSHALL, and J. MAYER. 1957. Effect of changes in ambient temperature on spontaneous activity, food intake, and body weight of goldthioglucose-obese and nonobese mice. Amer. Jour. Physiol., **188**:435.

FRIEDMAN, S. M., H. F. SCHERRER, M. NAKASHIMA, and C. L. FRIEDMAN. 1958. Extrarenal factors in diabetes insipidus in the rat. Amer. Jour. Physiol., **192**:401.

FROMMER, G. P. 1961. Electrophysiological analysis of gustatory, tongue temperature, and tactile representation in thalamus of albino rat. Ph.D. thesis, Brown University.

GEIGER, A., J. MAGNES, R. M. TAYLOR, and M. VERALLI. 1954. Effect of blood constituents on uptake of glucose and on metabolic rate of the brain in perfusion experiments. Amer. Jour. Physiol., **177**:138.

GILMAN, H. 1937. The relation between blood osmotic pressure, fluid distribution and voluntary water intake. Amer. Jour. Physiol., **120**:323.

GORDON, G., R. KITCHELL, L. STRÖM, and Y. ZOTTERMAN. 1959. The response pattern of taste fibres in the chorda tympani of the monkey. Acta Physiol. Scand., **46**:119.

GRAFE, E. 1923. Die pathologische Physiologie des Gesamtstoff- und Kraftwechels bei der Ernährung des Menschen. Ergebn. Physiol., **21** (Part II): 1.

GUILFORD, J. P. 1954. Psychometric Methods. McGraw-Hill Book Company, Inc., New York.

GUSEV, N. K. 1940a. Change of taste sensitivity in connection with a dynamic demand for food. Trudy instituta im. V.M. Bekhterova po izucheniyu mozga, **13**:156.

―――. 1940b. Intellectual mediation of taste sensations. *Ibid.*, p. 168.

GUTMAN, N. 1954. Operant conditioning, extinction, and periodic reinforcement in relation to concentration of sucrose used as reinforcement agent. Jour. Comp. Physiol. Psychol., **47**:358.

HAGSTROM, E. C., and C. PFAFFMANN. 1959. The relative taste effectiveness of different sugars for the rat. Jour. Comp. Physiol. Psychol., **52**:259.

HAHN, H., and H. GÜNTHER. 1932. Über die Reize und die Reizbedingungen des Geschmackssinnes. Pflüg. Arch. ges. Physiol., **231**:48.

HALE, E. B., and J. O. ALMQUIST. 1960. Relation of sexual behavior to germ cell output in farm animals. Symposium on Animal Reproduction. Supplement to Jour. Dairy Sci., **43**:145.

HALPERN, B. P. 1959. Gustatory responses in the medulla oblongata of the rat. Ph.D. thesis, Brown University.

HALPERN, B. P., R. A. BERNARD, and M. R. KARE. 1961. Gustatory nerve responses and preference behavior for amino acids in the rat. Fed. Proc., **20**(I):338.

HALPERN, B. P., and M. R. KARE. 1961. Neural responses to tongue stimulation in the domestic fowl (Abstract). Poultry Sci. (In press.)

HAMMAN, L., and I. I. HIRSCHMAN. 1919. Studies on blood sugar. IV. Effects upon the blood sugar of the repeated ingestion of glucose. Johns Hopkins Hosp. Bull., **30**:306.

HASLER, A. D. 1957. The sense organs: olfactory and gustatory senses of fishes. *In:* M. E. BROWN (ed.), The Physiology of Fishes. Academic Press, New York.

HERRING, P. T., J. C. IRVINE, and J. J. R. MACLEOD. 1924. The efficiency of various sugars and their derivatives in relieving the symptoms caused by insulin in mice. Biochem. Jour., **18**:1023.

HODGSON, E. S. 1955. Problems in invertebrate chemoreception. Quart. Rev. Biol., **30**:331.

IGGO, A. 1957. Gastric mucosal chemoreceptors with vagal afferent fibres in the cat. Quart. Jour. Exp. Physiol., **42**:398.

JACOBS, H. L. 1955. The motivation of sugar preferences in the albino rat. Ph.D. thesis, Cornell University.

————. 1958. Studies on sugar preference: I. The preference for glucose solutions and its modification by injections of insulin. Jour. Comp. Physiol. Psychol., **51**:304.

————. 1960. Non-metabolic factors in glucose appetite (Abstract). The Physiol., **3**:86.

————. 1961. Taste vs. "calories" as modulators of glucose intake. Fed. Proc., **20**(I):207.

JACOBS, H. L., and M. L. SCOTT. 1957. Factors mediating food and liquid intake in chickens. I. Studies on the preference for sucrose or saccharine solutions. Poultry Sci., **36**:8.

KAMEN, J., F. PILGRIM, N. GUTMAN, and B. KROLL. 1960. Interactions of suprathreshold taste stimuli. QMFCIAF, Rpt. 14–60, Prj. 7-84-15-007.

————. 1961. Interactions of suprathreshold taste qualities. Jour. Expt. Psychol. (In press.)

KARE, M. R., R. BLACK, and E. G. ALLISON. 1957. The sense of taste in the fowl. Poultry Sci., **36**:129.

KARE, M. R., B. P. HALPERN, and C. C. JONES. 1961. The influence of caloric deficiency on taste preference (Abstract). Poultry Sci. (In press.)

KARE, M. R., and W. MEDWAY. 1959. Discrimination between carbohydrates by the fowl. Poultry Sci., **38**:1119.

KARE, M. R., and H. PICK, JR. 1960. The influence of the sense of taste on feed and fluid consumption. Poultry Sci., **39**:697.

KARE, M. R., W. C. POND, and J. CAMPBELL. 1961. Variation in taste reactions among individual pigs. Animal Behaviour. (In press.)

KATZ, DAVID. 1953. Animals and Men. Pelican Books, Inc., Baltimore.

KENNEDY, G. C. 1950. The hypothalamic control of food intake in rats. Proc. Roy. Soc. London, B, **137**:535.

KIMURA, K., and L. M. BEIDLER. 1956. Microelectrode study of taste bud of the rat. Amer. Jour Physiol., **187**:610.

KISH, G. B. 1955. Learning when onset of illumination is used as reinforcing stimulus. Jour. Comp. Physiol. Psychol., **48**:261.

KITCHELL, R. L., L. STRÖM, and Y. ZOTTERMAN. 1959. Electrophysiological studies of thermal and taste reception in chickens and pigeons. Acta Physiol. Scand., **46**:133.

KLEIN, J. R., R. HURWITZ, and N. S. OLSEN. 1946. Distribution of intravenously injected fructose and glucose between blood and brain. Jour. Biol. Chem., **164**:509.

KLING, J. W., L. HOROWITZ, and J. E. DELHAGEN. 1956. Light as a positive reinforcer for rat responding. Psychol. Rept., **2**:337.

KROL'-LIVSHITS, D. E. 1933. Changes of thresholds of taste stimuli in dogs under influence of high external temperature. Arkhiv Biologicheskikh nauk., **33**:503.

————. 1935. Influence of temperature of solution on height of thresholds in dogs. Fiziologicheskiĭ Zhurnal SSSR, **18**:115.

KUJALOVÁ, V., and P. FÁBRY. 1960. Intestinal absorption of glucose, fat, and amino acids in rats adapted to intermittent starvation. Physiologica Bohemslovenica, **9**:35.

LANDGREN, S. 1957. Convergence of tactile, thermal, and gustatory impulses on single cortical cells. Acta Physiol. Scand., **40**:210.

————. 1960*a*. Thalamic neurones responding to cooling of the cat's tongue. *Ibid.*, **48**:255.

————. 1960*b*. Thalamic neurones responding to tactile stimulation of the cat's tongue. *Ibid.*, p. 238.

LAWRENCE, A. R., and L. N. FERGUSON. 1959. Exploratory physicochemical studies on the sense of taste. Nature, **183**:1469.

LINDENMAIER, P., and M. R. KARE. 1959. The taste end-organs of the chicken. Poultry Sci., **38**:545.

LUNDBAEK, K., and J. A. F. STEVENSON. 1948. The effect of previous carbohydrate deprivation on the carbohydrate metabolism of isolated muscle. Fed. Proc., **7**:75.

McCAY, C. M. 1958. The conservative attack upon problems of aging. Geriatrics, **13**:709.

McCAY, C. M., M. F. CROWELL, and L. A. MAYNARD. 1935. The effect of retarded growth upon the length of life span and upon the ultimate body size. Jour. Nutr., **10**:63.

McCLEARY, R. A. 1953. Taste and post-ingestion factors in specific-hunger behavior. Jour. Comp. Physiol. Psychol., **46**:411.

MAGEE, H. E., and E. REID. 1931. The absorption of glucose from the alimentary canal. Jour. Physiol., **73**:163.

MANDELSTAM, J., and J. YUDKIN. 1952. Studies in biochemical adaptation. The effect of variation in dietary protein upon the hepatic arginase of the rat. Biochem. Jour., **51**:681.

MARX, M. H., R. L. HENDERSON, and C. L. ROBERTS. 1955. Positive reinforcement of the bar-pressing response by a light stimulus following dark operant pre-tests with no after effect. Jour. Comp. Physiol. Psychol., **48**:73.

MAYER, J. 1953. Genetic, traumatic, and environmental factors in the etiology of obesity. Physiol. Rev., **33**:472.

MEYER, D. R. 1952. The stability of human gustatory sensitivity during changes in time of food deprivation. Jour. Comp. Physiol. Psychol., **45**:373.

MILLER, N. E., C. J. BAILEY, and J. A. STEVENSON. 1950. Decreased "hunger" but increased food intake resulting from hypothalamic lesions. Science, **112**:256.

Mochizuki, Y. 1939. Papilla foliata of Japanese. Folia Anat. Jap., **18**:337.

Moncrieff, R. W. 1946. The Chemical Senses. John Wiley & Sons, Inc., New York.

————. 1951. The Chemical Senses. Hill, London.

Moulton, D. G. 1960. Studies in olfactory acuity. V. The comparative olfactory sensitivity of pigmented and albino rats. Animal Behaviour, **8**:129.

Mountcastle, V. B., and E. Henneman. 1949. Pattern of tactile representation in thalamus of cat. Jour. Neurophysiol., **12**:85.

————. 1952. The representation of tactile sensibility in the thalamus of the monkey. Jour. Comp. Neurol., **97**:409.

Nachman, M. 1959. The inheritance of saccharin preference. Jour. Comp. Physiol. Psychol., **52**:451.

Nemanova, T. P. 1941. Conditioned reflexes to taste stimuli in children of the first months of life. Fiziologicheskiĭ Zhurnal SSSR, **30**:478.

Oakley, B. 1960. Electrophysiologically monitored lesions in the gustatory thalamic relay of the rat. M.S. thesis, Brown University.

————. 1961. Electrophysiologically monitored lesions in rat gustatory thalamic relay. Program, 32d Annual Meeting, Eastern Psychological Association, p. 43.

Odum, E. P. 1960. Premigratory hyperphagia in birds. Amer. Jour. Clin. Nutr., **8**:621.

O'Kelly, L. I., and J. L. Falk. 1958. Water regulation in the rat. II. The effects of preloads of water and sodium chloride on the bar-pressing performance of thirsty rats. Jour. Comp. Physiol. Psychol., **51**:22. ONR Report ACR-48. 1960. Bibliography on Saliva. Office of Naval Research.

Pangborn, R. M. 1960. Taste interrelationships. Food Res., **25**:245.

Parker, G. H. 1922. Smell, Taste and Allied Senses in the Vertebrates. J. B. Lippincott Co., Philadelphia.

Patton, H. D. 1960. Taste, olfaction and visceral sensation. *In:* T. Ruch and J. Fulton, Medical Physiology and Biophysics. W. B. Saunders and Co., Philadelphia.

Pfaffmann, C. 1936. Differential responses of the new-born cat to gustatory stimuli. Jour. Genet. Psychol., **49**:61.

————. 1939. Specific gustatory impulses. Jour. Physiol. (London), **96**:41P.

————. 1941. Gustatory afferent impulses. Jour. Cell. Comp. Physiol., **17**:243.

————. 1952. Taste preference and aversion following lingual denervation. Jour. Comp. Physiol. Psychol., **45**:393.

————. 1955. Gustatory nerve impulses in rat, cat, and rabbit. Jour. Neurophysiol., **18**:429.

————. 1959a. The afferent code for sensory quality. Amer. Psychol., **14**:226.

————. 1959b. The sense of taste. *In:* J. Field (ed.), Handbook of Physiology, Section 1, Vol. **1**. Amer. Physiol. Soc., Washington.

————. 1960. The pleasures of sensation. Psychol. Rev., **67**:253.

PFAFFMANN, C., and J. K. BARE. 1950. Gustatory nerve discharges in normal and adrenalectomized rats. Jour. Comp. Physiol. Psychol., **43**:320.

PFAFFMANN, C., R. P. ERICKSON, G. P. FROMMER, and B. P. HALPERN. 1961. Gustatory discharges in the rat medulla and thalamus. *In:* W. A. ROSEN-BLITH (ed.), Sensory Communication. John Wiley & Sons, Inc., New York.

PFAFFMANN, C., and E. C. HAGSTROM. 1955. Factors influencing taste sensitivity to sugar (Abstract). Amer. Jour. Physiol., **183**:651.

PICK, H., JR., and M. R. KARE. 1959. Certain aspects of taste preferences in chickens and calves. Amer. Psychol., **14**:572.

RICHTER, C. P. 1936. Increased salt appetite in adrenalectomized rats. Amer. Jour. Physiol., **115**:155.

————. 1939. Transmission of taste sensation in animals. Trans. Amer. Neurol. Assoc., **65**:49.

————. 1942. Increased dextrose appetite of normal rats treated with insulin. Amer. Jour. Physiol., **135**:781.

————. 1943. Total Self Regulatory Functions in Animals and Human Beings. Harvey Lectures, Science Press Printing Co., Lancaster, Pa.

RICHTER, C. P., and K. H. CAMPBELL. 1940. Sucrose taste thresholds of rats and humans. Amer. Jour. Physiol., **128**:291.

RICHTER, C. P., and J. F. ECKERT. 1937. Increased calcium appetite of parathyroidectomized rats. Endocrinol., **21**:50.

————. 1938. Mineral metabolism of adrenalectomized rats studied by the appetite method. *Ibid.*, **22**:214.

RICHTER, C. P., and E. SCHMIDT. 1941. Increased fat and decreased carbohydrate appetite of pancreatectomized rats. Endocrinol., **28**:179.

ROSE, J. E., and V. B. MOUNTCASTLE. 1952. The thalamic tactile region in rabbit and cat. Jour. Comp. Neurol., **97**:441.

ROSHUPKINA, A. I. 1954. Experimental material on the physiology of the taste analyzer. Thesis for the degree of candidate of science, on deposit in Lenin Library in Moscow.

SAKHIULINA, G. T. 1945. Character of electrical potentials of the glossopharyngeal nerve under taste stimulation of the tongue. Biyull. Eksp. Biolog. i. Med., **19**:66.

SCHREIBER, G. A. 1887. Concerning the dependence of taste sensations on the territory of the taste organ and the temperature of the taste substances. Dissertation, Moscow.

SCHUTZ, H. G., and F. J. PILGRIM. 1957. Sweetness of various compounds and its measurement. Food Res., **22**:206.

SHUFORD, E. 1959. Palatability and osmotic pressure of glucose and sucrose solutions as determinants of intake. Jour. Comp. Physiol. Psychol., **52**:150.

SILBERBERG, R., S. R. JARRETT, and M. SILBERBERG. 1961. Life span of mice fed enriched or restricted diets during growth. Amer. Jour. Physiol., **200**:332.

SKINNER, B. F. 1953. Science and Human Behavior. Macmillan Co., New York.

SOEDARMO, D., M. R. KARE, and R. H. WASSERMAN. 1961. Observations on the removal of sugars from the mouth and the crop of the chicken. Poultry Sci., **40**:123.

SOULAIRAC, A. 1947. La physiologie d'un comportement: L'appétit glucidique et sa régulation neuro-endocrinienne chez les rongeurs. Biol. Bull. Fr. et Belg., **81**:272.

————. 1950. Le rôle de l'estomac dans le mécanisme physiologique de l'appétit pour les glucides. C. R. Acad. Sci., Paris, **231**:73.

STELLAR, E., R. HYMAN, and S. SAMET. 1954. Gastric factors controlling water and salt-solution drinking. Jour. Comp. Physiol. Psychol., **47**:220.

STEWART, J. 1960. Reinforcing effects of light as a function of intensity and reinforcement schedule. Jour. Comp. Physiol. Psychol., **53**:187.

SUNDERLAND, S., and A. F. ROCHE. 1958. Axon-myelin relationships in peripheral nerve fibres. Acta Anat., **33**:1.

SWANN, H. G., and B. J. PENNER. 1939. The effect of salts on the diabetes insipidus following post-hypophysectomy in the rat. Endocrinol., **24**:253.

TEITELBAUM, P. 1955. Sensory control of hypothalamic hyperphagia. Jour. Comp. Physiol. Psychol., **48**:156.

TEPPERMAN, H. M., and J. TEPPERMAN. 1958. The hexosemonophosphate shunt and adaptive hyperlipogenesis. Diabetes, **7**:478.

TEPPERMAN, J., J. R. BROBECK, and C. N. H. LONG. 1943. The effects of hypothalamic hyperphagia and of alterations in feeding habits on the metabolism of the albino rat. Yale Jour. Biol. and Med., **15**:855.

TEPPERMAN, J., H. M. TEPPERMAN, and M. P. SCHULMAN. 1956. Oxidation of palmitic acid-1-C^{14} by tissues of carbohydrate and fat diet-adapted rats. Amer. Jour. Physiol., **184**:80.

TIMOFEEV, N. V., and D. E. KROL'-LIVSHITS. 1933. Change of sharpness of taste in workers under conditions of work in several industries and under diseases with loss of secretion of gastric juices. Archiv. Biologicheskikh nauk., **33** (No. 3–4):481.

TITLEBAUM, L. F., J. L. FALK, and J. MAYER. 1960. Altered acceptance and rejection of NaCl in rats with diabetes insipidus. Amer. Jour. Physiol., **199**:22.

TORNIVA, A. I. 1940. Toward the question of the influence of extraneous stimuli on change of taste sensitivity. Trudȳ instituta im. V.M. Bekhterova po izucheniyu mozga, **13**:175.

TORREY, T. W. 1940. The influence of nerve fibers upon taste buds during embryonic development. Proc. Nat. Acad. Sci., **26**:627.

TOSTESON, D. C., M. DEFRIEZ, M. ABRAMS, C. W. GOTTSCHALK, and E. M. LANDIS. 1951. Effects of adrenalectomy, desoxycorticosterone acetate and increased fluid intake on intake of sodium chloride and bicarbonate by hypertensive and normal rats. Amer. Jour. Physiol., **164**:369.

UFLAND, J. M. 1928. Veränderungen des Geshmacksschärfe bei Bleiarbeiten. Zeitschrift f. Sinnesphysiologie, **59**:128.

VARGA, F. 1959. The respective effects of starvation and changed body composition on energy metabolism in malnourished infants. Pediatrics, **23**:1085.

VASILYEV, A. I. 1957. A complex method of study of the functioning of the taste analyzer in man. Trudy instituta fiziologii. im. I. P. Pavlova, **6**:172.

————. 1959. On bilateral activity of the parotid salivary glands in man. Fiziologicheskii Zhurnal SSSR, **45**:24.

VERNEY, E. B. 1947. The antidiuretic hormone and the factors which determine its release. Proc. Roy. Soc. London, B, **135**:25.

WALL, P. D. 1960. Cord cells responding to touch, damage, and temperature of skin. Jour. Neurophysiol., **23**:197.

WARREN, R. P., and C. PFAFFMANN. 1959. Early experience and taste aversion. Jour. Comp. Physiol. Psychol., **52**:263.

WATTS, D. T., and D. R. H. GOURLEY. 1953. A simple apparatus for determining basal metabolism of small animals in student laboratory. Proc. Soc. Exp. Biol. Med., **84**:585.

WEBER, W., R. O. DAVIES, and M. R. KARE. 1960. Distribution of taste buds and changes with age in the ruminant. Unpublished data.

WEDDELL, G. 1955. Somesthesis and the chemical senses. Ann. Rev. Psychol., **6**:119.

WEINER, I. H., and E. STELLAR. 1951. Salt preference of the rat determined by a single-stimulus method. Jour. Comp. Physiol. Psychol., **44**:394.

WELKER, W. I. 1960. Ontogeny of exploratory behavior. *In:* Symposium: Exploratory Behavior and Responses to Novel Stimuli: Recent Developments. Amer. Psychol., **15**:484.

WEVER, E. G. 1949. Theory of Hearing. John Wiley & Sons, Inc., New York.

WIERZUCHOWSKI, M. 1937. Oxidation of glucose as function of its supply. Jour. Physiol. (London), **90**:440.

WILKINS, L., and C. P. RICHTER. 1940. A great craving for salt by a child with cortico-adrenal insufficiency. Jour. Amer. Med. Assoc., **114**:866.

YOUNG, P. T. 1944. Studies of food preference, appetite, and dietary habit. I. Running activity and dietary habit of the rat in relation to food preference. Jour. Comp. Psychol., **37**:327.

————. 1949. Palatability vs. appetite as determinants of the critical concentrations of sucrose and sodium chloride. Comp. Psychol. Monograph, **19**:1.

————. 1957. Psychologic factors regulating the feeding process. Jour. Clin. Nutr., **5**:154.

————. 1957*a*. Continuous recording of the fluid-intake of small animals. Amer. Jour. Psychol., **70**:295.

————. 1959. The role of affective processes in learning and motivation. Psychol. Rev., **66**:104.

————. 1960. Isohedonic contour maps. Psychol. Rept., **7**:478.

YOUNG, P. T., and J. P. CHAPLIN. 1949. Studies of food preference, appetite, and dietary habit. X. Preferences of adrenalectomized rats for salt solutions of different concentrations. Comp. Psychol. Monograph, **19**:45.

YOUNG, P. T., and J. L. FALK. 1956. The relative acceptability of sodium chloride solutions as a function of concentration and water need. Jour. Comp. Physiol. Psychol., **49**:569.

YOUNG, P. T., and J. T. GREENE. 1953. Quantity of food ingested as a measure of relative acceptability. Jour. Comp. Physiol. Psychol., **46**:288.

YOUNG, P. T., and H. W. RICHEY. 1952. Diurnal drinking patterns in the rat. Jour. Comp. Physiol. Psychol., **45**:80.

ZOTTERMAN, Y. 1935. Action potentials in the glossopharyngeal nerve and in the chorda tympani. Scand. Arch. Physiol., **72**:73.

———. 1949. The response of the frog's taste fibres to the application of pure water. Acta Physiol. Scand., **18**:181.

———. 1956. Species differences in the water taste. *Ibid.*, **37**:60.

———. 1958. Studies in the nervous mechanism of taste. *In:* H. FERNÁNDEZ-MORÁN and R. BROWN (eds.). The Submicroscopic Organization and Function of Nerve Cells. Academic Press, New York. (Exp. Cell. Res. [Suppl. 5], 1958.)

ZOTTERMAN, Y., and H. DIAMANT. 1959. Has water a specific taste? Nature, **183**:191.

ZUBKOVA, N. A. 1959. Change in activity of the taste analyzer under experimental gastritis in dogs. Nauchnaya soobsheniya instituta im. I. P. Pavlova 95.

ZUIDEMA, G., N. P. CLARKE, and M. MINTON. 1956. Osmotic regulation of body fluids. Amer. Jour. Physiol., **187**:85.

Index

Acetic acid, neural responses to, 43, 44, 47–48, 74

Adaptation, 39, 41

Addison's disease, influence on sodium-chloride selection, 93–94

Adrenalectomy, influence on sodium-chloride selection, 93–94, 99, 101, 102, 115

After-discharge, 40

After tastes, from electrical stimulation, 122

Age, effect of, on taste response, 7, 30–32

Alloxan, influence on food selection, 99

Amphibians, chemoreceptors of, 6

Anthranilate (Di-methyl), rejection by chicken, 11–12

Animal: need-free, 91; non-deprived, 90

Arabinose, preference for, 8

Birds, anatomical and dietary changes in, 113

Bitterness, of mixtures, 70–71

Caffeine, in mixtures, 69–71, 74

Calcium, preference for, 93, 102

Calf: individual differences, 12–13, 35; response to acids of, 118; to quinine, 118; to sodium chloride, 118; to sugars, 8, 12, 16, 118, 127

Caloric restriction, effect of: on metabolism, 106–8, 109; on mortality, 111–12

Calories, relation to preference, 26, 27, 28

Carbohydrates, effect on metabolism of, 104–8

Cat: discrimination of sodium chloride, 32; preference for sucrose, 14, 30, 35–36

Central nervous system, taste relays in; *see* Cortex; Medulla; Taste response; Thalamus

Chemical senses, evolution of, 6

Chemical structure, relation to taste reaction, 8, 37, 73, 77, 127

Chemoreception: internal, 10, 11, 27, 28, 100, 101, 115, 127; survival value of, 7, 127

Chicken: drinking behavior in, 30; gustatory neural response in, 29, 41, 42; preference

for sodium chloride, 29; reaction to sugar, 8–10, 12, 30–31, 35; taste buds in, 7, 28, 29

Chorda tympani; fibers, 39; taste responses, ix, 30, 32, 33, 39, 42, 43, 46, 51, 54, 55, 56, 57, 61–64, 74, 76, 94

Circumvallate papillae, effects of stroking, on taste, 43–44

Citric acid: effect in mixtures, 68–71, 74; gustatory neural responses to, 74–75

Colchicine, effect on cells of, 30

Common chemical sense, 6

Conditioned-response technique, 118, 120

Cortex (cerebral), gustatory relay, 50, 59, 60, 61

Cow, taste in, 118, 119

Crop, chemical discrimination by, 10

Diabetes insipidus, effect on sodium-chloride preference of, 100–101

Diet, relation to disease, 97

Dietary changes, relation to taste of, 15

Discrimination thresholds, 118, 119, 120, 121

Disease, effect on taste sensitivity of, 123

Distilled water, odor of, 88

Dogs, taste in, 118, 119, 123, 125

Early experience, effect on taste preference, 33–34

Enzymes: relation to food intake, 95, 96, 98; taste theory based upon, 8

Ethylene glycol, neural responses to, 42, 47, 48

Eyelid response, conditioned, use in experiments of, 119

Facial nerve, 121; *see also* Chorda tympani

Ferric chloride, response to, by chicks, 13

Fish, taste organs of, 6

Fluid intake, relation to diet, 35–36

Food intake: influence of taste on, 12, 36; regulators of, 16–26, 36, 132

Fructose, preference for, 8, 12, 98

Galactose, 8, 103

Gastric capacity, relation to food intake, 36–37, 109, 111, 112, 113

Glossopharyngeal nerve, 29, 30, 38, 41–48, 61, 62, 94, 121

Glucose, neural responses to, 32

Glucose, preference for, 8–9, 17, 18, 20, 21, 22, 24, 25, 26, 93

Glycerin, neural responses to, 41–43

Goat, neural responses in, 43–44, 50

Goldthioglucose, 37, 111, 112

Guinea pig, rejection of "bitter" taste by, 32

Gustatory neural response: in chicken, 41–42; in man, 46–47; in monkey, 41–43, 45

Hamster, preference for sucrose, 14, 16

Homeostasis, environmental, 93

Hunger: effect on taste sensitivity, 122–23; specific, 103

Hydrochloric acid, neural responses to, ix, 53–56

Hyperphagia: in birds, 113–14; in thalamic lesions, 65

Hypothalamic lesions: influence on food selection, 36–37; resulting hyperphagia, 36–37, 116

Insulin, effect on food selection, 92–93, 98–99, 115

Integrator, summator technique, 40, 51, 53, 75, 129

Intestine, chemical discrimination by, 10

Isohedons, 82–86

Learning, 33–35, 73, 78

Lesions: effect on preference, 50, 59, 60–61, 65; hypothalamic, 111

Longevity, influence of food intake on, 110–11

Man, infant: neural response in, 46, 47; taste sensitivity in, 32, 119

Mannitol, 27

Mannose, preference for, 8

Mechanical stimulation of tongue, responses to, 29, 47, 51, 52, 58, 59, 61, 63, 64

Medulla oblongata: gustatory neural activity, 51–52, 54–57, 59, 63–64, 75, 115; relay, 52, 59, 63, 64

Metabolic mixture, 92, 94, 97–98

Metabolism, 21, 92–95, 104–9, 111

Methionine, preference for, 34

Mixtures, effect of, on taste responses, 66–72, 73, 74–75, 122

Monkey, neural response in, 42–43, 45

Motivation, x–xi, 67, 89, 102

Mouth, absorption of sugar from, 11

Nerve fibers: firing frequency, 39; measurement of size, 48

Neural response, methods of quantifying, 40

Novelty, reward effect of, 91

Nutrition, 7, 92–94

Obesity, 36, 37, 96, 97, 109–13, 116, 132; hypothalamic, 36–37, 96, 111–12, 116; physiological, 113–14

Occupation, influence on taste sensitivity, 124

Odor, influence of, on taste preference, 88–89

Olfaction, relation to pigmentation, 38

Osmotic pressure, relation to preference, 17–22, 24, 26–28, 31, 87, 128

Oxygen deficiency, influence on preference, 123

Pancreatectomy, influence on food choice of, 92, 98

Parathyroidectomy, influence on food choice of, 93

Patterning, of sensory input, ix–x, 37, 39, 73

Pheasant, taste in, 32

Pigeon: gustatory neural response in, 45–46, 48; rejection of quinine by, 49

Pigmentation, relation to chemoreception, 38

Pigs, preference of: for quinine sulphate, 12–13; for saccharin, 12–13, 77; for sucrose, 12–13

Postingestion factors, 17, 22, 26–27, 128

Potassium chloride, gustatory neural responses to, 53–56

Preference: individual differences, 12–15, 32, 35, 128; species differences, 14–16, 77, 127

Preference test: brief exposure, 22, 80–82; graphic method, 79; 8–9, 16–17, 35, 79; short-term, 16, 17, 35; single bottle, 18, 20, 22, 119, 121

Psychophysics, in taste, 67, 74, 76, 77, 83

Quinine: effect in mixtures, 82; neural responses to, 41–44, 47, 53–56; preference for, xi, 12–13, 34–35, 37–38, 49–50, 59

Quinine hydrochloride, odor of, 88

Rabbit, preference of, for sucrose, 14, 16

Rat, preference of: for glucose, 18, 20–22, 24–26; for sodium chloride, 17, 38, 59, 87–88; for sucrose, 16; for sugar, 14, 59

Rat, response of: to sodium chloride, 33, 51–56, 101; to sugar, 32–33, 53–56

Rating scale, 67–68

Receptor cells, ix–x, 7

Receptor mechanism, auxiliary, 10

Riboflavin, influence on food choice of, 94

Ringer's solution, response to, 41–42, 45–47

Saccharin: gustatory neural responses to, 33, 40, 42–43, 47–48; preference for, 12–13, 27–28, 33, 59, 77

Saccharin preference, genetic basis of, 33

Saliva flow, 118, 121, 123, 125

Saltiness, of mixtures, 69–71

Satiation, 18, 20, 22, 27

Satiety, 18, 20, 22–27, 90

Sea anemone, 6

Senses: Aristotelian theory of, 1; Locke's theory of, 2; philosophic history of, 1

Single-unit responses: central nervous system, 50, 58, 63, 72; peripheral, ix–x, 30, 40, 72–74

Sodium bicarbonate, neural responses to, 43–44

Sodium chloride: effects of excess, 99–101, 115; in mixtures, 70, 74, 83–87; neural responses to, 33, 41–47, 50, 52–54, 56, 76, 101; preference for, 29, 38, 59, 86–88, 93, 100, 102, 115

Solvent, response to, 41–42; *see also* Water responses, 45

Sourness, of mixtures, 71, 74, 75

Spontaneous activity, thalamic, 52, 53

Stereoisomers, 8

Stimuli, method of applying, 40–41

Stomach contents, effect on preference of, 20–26

Sucrose: in mixtures, 70, 74–75, 82–87; neural responses to, x, 32–33, 42–48, 53–56, 74; odor of, 88; preference for, 8–9, 12, 16, 18, 30–31, 35, 59, 86, 92, 98–99

Sucrose octa-acetate, preference for, 33–34

Sweetness: of mixtures, 66, 69–70, 71, 74, 75, 77; relation of caloric value to, 28; of sugars, 77, 99

Taste, role of: in metabolic adaptations, 132; in nutritional adaptations, 132

Taste blindness, 32–33

Taste buds: histology, 6; in calves, 7; in chicken, 7, 32, 37; influence of age on number of, 7, 32; location of, 6, 29; mitosis of, ix, 30; number of, 7, 10, 28, 32, 37–38; in rats, dogs, calves, pigs, chickens, 6

Taste discrimination, influence of odor on, 88

Taste preference, influence on total intake of, 127

Taste qualities: application to animals of, 77; confusion of, 70, 72; interactions of, 66–71; number and basis of, viii–ix, 28, 66, 72–73, 76–78, 125–26, 131; spatial representation of, 54–55

Taste response, rating scale for, 67–68

Taste solutions, methods of application of, 41

Temperature: effect on taste of, 125; external effect on taste sensitivity of, 123; responses to, 29, 41, 51, 58, 64

Thalamus, gustatory neural activity of, 50–58, 61–62, 64; relay, 50, 57–59, 60–64, 131–32

Thiamine, 94, 102–3

Thirst, relation to stomach contents, 17, 20, 22–26

Tongue, pre-stimulus treatment, 41

Toxicity, 8, 10

Trigeminal nerve, responses, 29, 64, 94, 121

Unconditioned-response technique, 118

Urea, use of, as stomach load, 21, 22

Vagus nerve, 29, 121

Viscosity, influence on preference, 8, 30, 31

Vitamin B, influence on food choice, 94

Water deprivation, relation to preference of, 23–26

Water responses, neural, 41–43, 45–46, 77

X-ray radiation, effect on chorda tympani responses of, ix

Xylose: rejection in chicken of, 10–11; toxicity of, 9

PRINTED IN U.S.A.